NUMERICAL METHODS IN GEOMECHANICS / INNSBRUCK / 1988

PROCEEDINGS OF THE SIXTH INTERNATIONAL CONFERENCE ON NUMERICAL METHODS IN GEOMECHANICS / INNSBRUCK / 11-15 APRIL 1988

Numerical Methods in Geomechanics Innsbruck 1988

Edited by
G.SWOBODA
Institute of Structural Engineering, University of Innsbruck

VOLUME FOUR:
Invited lectures
Late papers
Index

Published on behalf of the International Committee for Numerical Methods in Geomechanics by

A.A.BALKEMA / ROTTERDAM / BROOKFIELD / 1989

ORGANIZING COMMITTEES

International Conference Committee

Prof. G.Swoboda (Chairman) University of Innsbruck, Austria
Prof. C.S.Desai (Co-Chairman) University of Arizona, USA
Prof. H.Duddeck (Co-Chairman) Technical University of Braunschweig, FR Germany
Prof. W.Wittke (Co-Chairman) Technical University of Aachen, FR Germany
Prof. T.Adachi, Kyoto University, Japan
Prof. D.Aubry, Ecole Centrale des Arts, France
Dr. G.Beer, CSIRO, Division Geomechanics, Australia
Prof. Y.K.Cheung, University of Hong Kong, Hong Kong
Prof. G.Clough, Virginia State University, USA
Dr. J.T.Christian, Stone & Webster Engineer Corp., USA
Prof. W.D.L.Finn, University of British Columbia, Canada
Prof. G.Gioda, Politecnico di Milano, Italy
Prof. G.Gudehus, Technical University of Karlsruhe, FR Germany
Prof. Y.Ichikawa, Nagoya University, Japan
Prof. K.Kovári, ETH-Hönggerberg, Switzerland
Prof. Y.M.Lin, Northeast University, People's Republic of China
Prof. S.Ukhov, Moscow Civil Engineering Institute, USSR
Prof. F.Medina, Universidad de Chile, Chile
Prof. Z.Mróz, Polish Academy of Science, Poland
Prof. J.Prevost, Princeton University, USA
Prof. J.Smith, University of Manchester, UK
Prof. C.Tanimoto, Kyoto University, Japan
Prof. S.Valliappan, University of New South Wales, Australia
Prof. A.Varadarajan, ITT, Delhi, India
Prof. S.J.Wang, Academia Sinica, People's Republic of China
Prof. N.E.Wiberg, Chalmers University of Technology, Sweden
Prof. O.C.Zienkiewicz, University of Wales, UK

International Committee for Numerical Methods in Geomechanics

Prof. T.Adachi, Japan
Prof. D.Aubry, France
Prof. A.S.Balasubramaniam, Thailand
Prof. J.R.Booker, Australia
Dr. C.A.Brebbia, UK
Prof. Y.K.Cheung, Hong Kong
Dr. J.T.Christian, USA
Dr. A.Cividini, Italy
Prof. C.S.Desai, USA (Chairman)
Prof. J.M.Duncan, USA
Prof. Z.Eisenstein, Canada
Prof. A.J.Ferrante, Brazil
Prof. W.D.L.Finn, Canada
Dr. J.Geertsma, Netherlands
Prof. J.Ghaboussi, USA
Prof. K.Höeg, Norway
Prof. K.Ishihara, Japan
Prof. T.Kawamoto, Japan
Prof. K.Kovári, Switzerland
Prof. S.Prakash, India
Prof. J.M.Roesset, USA
Prof. I.M.Smith, UK
Prof. V.I.Solomin, USSR
Prof. G.Swoboda, Austria
Prof. S.Valliappan, Australia
Prof. C.Viggiani, Italy
Prof. S.Wang, People's Republic of China
Prof. N.E.Wiberg, Sweden
Prof. W.Wittke, FR Germany
Prof. O.C.Zienkiewicz, UK

The texts of the various papers in this volume were set individually by typists under the supervision of each of the authors concerned.

Published by

A.A.Balkema, P.O.Box 1675, 3000 BR Rotterdam, Netherlands

A.A.Balkema Publishers, Old Post Road, Brookfield, VT 05036, USA

For the complete set of four volumes ISBN 90 6191 809 X
For volume 1: ISBN 90 6191 810 3
For volume 2: ISBN 90 6191 811 1
For volume 3: ISBN 90 6191 812 X
For volume 4: ISBN 90 6191 830 8

Printed in the Netherlands

Numerical Methods in Geomechanics (Innsbruck 1988), Swoboda (ed.)
© 1989 Balkema, Rotterdam. ISBN 90 6191 809 X

Contents

Invited lectures

Late papers

Invited lectures

Numerical Methods in Geomechanics (Innsbruck 1988), Swoboda (ed.)
© 1989 Balkema, Rotterdam. ISBN 90 6191 809 X

Application of 3-D boundary element and coupled analysis in geomechanics: Case studies

G.Beer
CSIRO, Division of Geomechanics, Brisbane, Australia

ABSTRACT: Applications of boundary element and coupled boundary element/finite element analysis to problems in geomechanics are shown. The emphasis is on three-dimensional analyses and applications in mining and tunnelling. A conclusion of the paper is that such analyses are extremely efficient tools for prediction and "trouble shooting" in geotechnical engineering.

1 INTRODUCTION

Whilst most engineers are familiar with the Finite Element Method (F.E.M.) the Boundary Element Method (B.E.M.) is not so well-known. It has been, and still is, the "cinderella" of numerical methods mainly because it has had a much more mathematical "ancestry" than the F.E.M. Most text books on the B.E.M. are too difficult to understand for the average civil or geotechnical engineer, who probably has - in his many years in practice - long forgotten what he may have learned about integral equations, and Cauchy principal values. In the writer's opinion, there is no reason why such fancy mathematics are employed in some text books as the method can be explained using simple engineering principles such as Betti's reciprocal theorem and the method of superposition[1].

The fact that the B.E.M. is not so well known as its "big sister" the F.E.M. is unfortunate because it is so ideally suited for problems in geomechanics. Its major advantage is that it can deal with infinite and semi-infinite domains. Also, the amount of input data required to describe a problem is reduced dramatically, especially in three-dimensions, because only boundary surfaces have to be discretised.

These features of the B.E.M. make it an extremely efficient tool for the analysis of problems in geomechanics, in particular, in mining applications. In a typical regional model of a mine up to 30 excavations may have to be considered in the analysis. The task involved in making a three-dimensional Finite Element model of such a complex mine geometry is considerable, not only due to the fact that the rock mass between the excavations has to be discretised, but also due to the necessity to apply "artificial" boundary conditions at the boundaries of the mesh far enough away from the excavations. The task of generating a three-dimensional Finite Element mesh between the excavations, which may be of quite complex shape, is extremely arduous and time consuming. The writer has heard of cases where man-months have been spent to specify three-dimensional meshes.

In contrast to this, the three-dimensional B.E.M. mesh shown in case study No. 1 took a young mining engineer who was never previously exposed to numerical modelling only 2 days to input and to obtain the results. With interactive graphical pre-processing on graphics workstations this time will be reduced to a couple of hours in the near future.

One of the main criticisms of the B.E.M has been that, if a boundary discretisation is used, the continuum is assumed to behave linearly elastic and to have isotropic and homogenous material properties. Unfortunately, geomaterials such as rock and soil rarely behave elastically and can, in most cases, not be assumed to be isotropic and homogenous. The rock mass contains joints and fractures and is, in general, anisotropic. Also, most deformations will occur in the inelastic range. It is well known that the modelling of such material behaviour presents no difficulty to the F.E.M. The most optimal way of analysing such problems, it seems, is by a combination of the Boundary and the Finite Element method.

This coupling of B.E. and F.E. meshes was proposed about ten years ago by O. Zienkiewicz in his now famous paper 'Marriage a la mode'[2]. Indeed, in such an analysis the engineer can have the "best of both worlds", i.e. the user friendliness of the Boundary Element method and the versatility of the Finite Element method.

Over the last 10 years the writer has developed a two- and three-dimensional stress analysis program (BEFE) which can use either the Boundary Element, Finite Element or coupled method of analysis[3].

Without going to too much detail (which is given in [4]) the coupling algorithm in BEFE works on the principle of obtaining a stiffness matrix of the interface nodes (i.e. the nodes where the connection to Finite Elements occurs). There are two main energy methods which are used for this purpose: the principle of virtual work and the principle of minimum potential energy. Surprisingly they give different answers. The former results in an unsymmetric stiffness matrix the latter in a symmetric one. Mang et al.[5,6] have shown that this is because of approximations introduced by the boundary element discretisation and that the difference vanishes with increased mesh refinement. Tests by the author[7] on fairly coarse coupled meshes have shown that for geometries encountered in geotechnical problems (infinite domain) the difference is negligible and mainly occurs at the interface between the two discretisations.

The main reasons the writer prefers the symmetric approach is that the Finite Element part of program BEFE uses a symmetric frontal solver. This solver has the advantage that only half the stiffness matrix (including all the diagonal terms) need to be stored and operated upon. As the interface stiffness matrix is fully populated and - for most practical examples - large, this results in a more economic use of computer resources and is in the authors opinion essential for the practical applications discussed here.

2 MODELLING PHILOSOPHY: BOUNDARY ELEMENTS ONLY VS COUPLED ANALYSIS

There are basically three ways in which excavations in rock can be modelled.

(1) Boundary Elements only.
(2) Partially coupled with Finite Element.
(3) Fully coupled with Finite Elements.

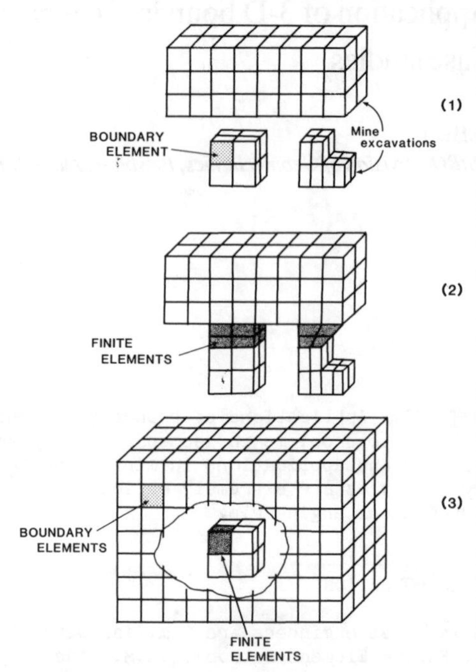

Figure 1. Different strategies for modelling excavations in rock
(1) Boundary Elements only,
(2) partially coupled,
(3) fully coupled.

The methods are listed in increasing complexity and increased requirement of man and computing resources. Examples are shown in Figure 1 on a mining excavation problem. For modelling procedure (1) only the surfaces of the excavation have to be modelled but the rock mass is assumed to be elastic. This means that no stress redistribution due to yielding of the rock and movements on joints occurs.

Approach (2) goes some way towards modelling of inelastic deformations in the rock mass. There, only the regions of the rock mass which are assumed to be highly stressed are discretised into Finite Elements. If the regions chosen are indeed the only ones experiencing inelastic behaviour, this partially coupled mesh will give the correct answer for the nonlinear problem. If, as would in general be the case, other regions of the mesh which have not been discretised into Finite Elements yield also then a fully coupled analysis (3) is required. The analyses are of increased complexity and mesh (3) approaches the input requirement of a Finite Element mesh. However, because Boundary Elements are used on the boundaries of the Finite Element mesh there is no need to apply "artificial" boundary conditions and the F.E. mesh need not be extended beyond the region of interest.

Apart from an increase of resources in data preparation there is also an increase in computing resources required for the analysis from method 1 to 3.

The coupling method described in [4] requires five steps:

(1) Establish Boundary Element Equations.

$$\mathbf{B}\ \mathbf{x} = \mathbf{f} + \mathrm{A}\ \mathbf{a} \qquad (1)$$

Where **B** and **A** are coefficient matrices, **x** is a vector of unknown and **f** a vector of known values. Finally **a** contains displacements at interface nodes.

(2) Solve B.E. Equations. Next the B.E. equations are solved by treating each column of **A** as a right hand side vector. The solutions are the displacement at the free nodes and the tractions at the interface nodes due to zero and unit displacements at the interface.

(3) Determine Interface stiffness matrix using virtual work or minimum potential energy principles. The stiffness matrix will be fully populated, i.e. each node at the interface will affect the other.

(4) Assemble Interface stiffness matrix with the Finite Element stiffness matrices and solve for unknown displacements.

(5) Back substitute interface displacements into equation (1) and solve for unknown displacements/tractions at all nodes of the mesh.

It is obvious that the higher the degree of coupling, the higher the number of interface degree of freedom, and as a consequence more right hand sides will have to be considered. Also, since the stiffness matrix is fully populated, the front width of the final (global) system to be solved will increase.

For large 3-D coupled systems an implementation on a supercomputer is desirable. In particular, it is relatively easy to vectorise the inner DO-loops of the frontal solution program resulting in an increase in speed by a factor of 100-200 compared with minicomputers.

The computer program BEFE is currently installed on VAX mini computers and a CDC supercomputer (vectorised version).

For the examples shown below computing times for both the CYBER 205 supercomputer and, if available, on the VAX minicomputer are given.

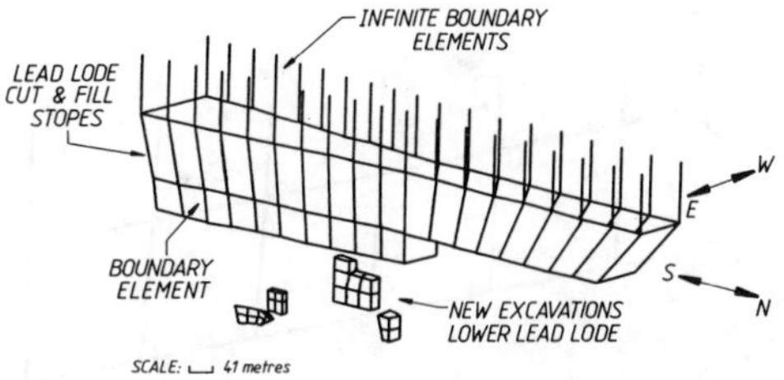

Figure 2. Boundary Element mesh for mine planning study.

3 CASE STUDIES

Four case studies will be discussed which demonstrate the three approaches to modelling discussed above. They cover application in both mining and tunnelling.

3.1 Case study 1: mining planning study at Z.C. Mine, Broken Hill

Z.C. Mine is a large lead-silver-zinc mine in the southern part of Australia. It is one of the older Australian mines and has used a wide variety of excavation methods.

The case study[10] involves the planning for future extraction of ore below 1000 m underground. Different planning strategies were proposed and the role of the analysis was to help select the most appropriate one. The results expected from the analysis were the location of highly stressed areas such as crown and regional pillars and stress magnitudes there.

The mesh involving linear Boundary Elements only is shown in Figure 2.

The mesh includes the old mining areas which extend about 1000 m to the surface and have been discretised into linear boundary elements and infinite boundary elements. The infinite boundary elements are special elements which can be used to represent surfaces which extend to infinity or, as in this case, a long way to the surface. Infinite Boundary elements, which are described in detail in [8] and [9], are a very efficient way of describing such surfaces.

Altogether there were 15 different stages of extraction to be modelled and Figure 2 shows one of these stages. The results are displayed in Figure 3 as contours of deviatoric stress ($\sigma_{max}-\sigma_{min}$) which is significant for rock mass strength.

It can be seen that major stress concentrations occur at the top of the L-shaped

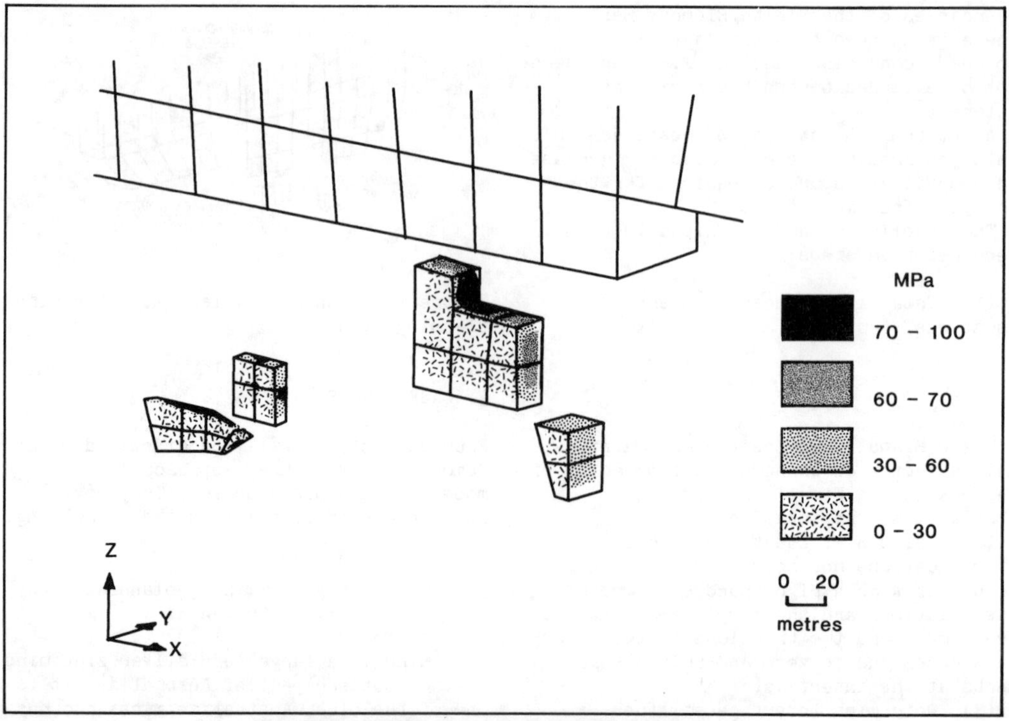

Figure 3. Results of analysis displayed as contours of deviatoric stress on new excavation surfaces

excavation at the re-entrant corners, and between the excavations on the lower left side. A typical excavation stage took 1 hour on a MicroVAX computer and 140 seconds on a CYBER 205 supercomputer.

3.2 Case study 2: backanalysis study: Mt Charlotte Mine

The Mt Charlotte Mine is a large underground gold mine in Western Australia.

The rock mass is fairly strong and competent but is transsected by major faults. One of the significant faults is termed Beta fault. In 1985 a seismic event caused by slip on Beta Fault occurred during blasting of an excavation. In 1987 a study was commissioned by the mine management via James Askew and Associates to ascertain the reasons for the event by backanalysing the excavation geometry prior and after the slip occurred.

Figure 4 shows a perspective view of the meshes for the three excavation stages modelled. The meshes consist of two boundary element regions which are connected by joint Finite Elements representing the Beta Fault. As the actual extent of Beta Fault was unknown infinite Boundary Elements were used at the periphery of the mesh in the fault plane. Details of the assumptions made and the results obtained from the analysis are reported in [11].

3.3 Case study 3: fully coupled analysis of a mine excavation

This case study relates to an excavation at the Rosebery Mine in Tasmania, an island south of the Australian mainland. In contrast to the previous two case studies the rock mass is fractured and contains several sets of closely spaced joints. Therefore, it was important to model the nonlinear behaviour of the rock mass, i.e. slip and dilation on joint planes near the excavation.

The particular excavation modelled represents a trial stope which was to be extensively monitored after the analysis. The reason for the analysis was to assist in selecting the most optimal location of the monitoring equipment.

The fully coupled mesh used for the analysis is shown in Figure 5. The mesh has been cut open to reveal the Finite Elements representing the "near field"

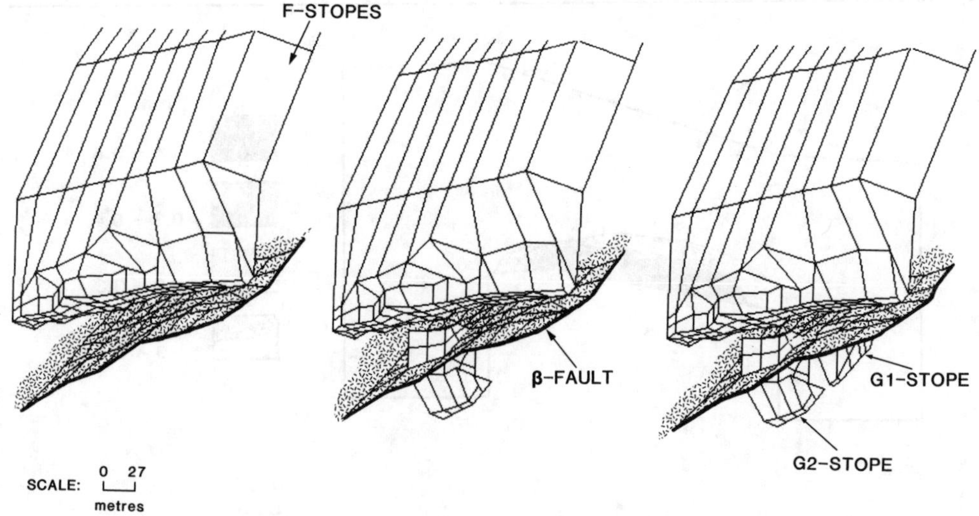

Figure 4. Mt Charlotte Mine: different excavation stages modelled.

rock and the excavation itself. For the Finite Elements a multi-laminate model[12] with one plane of weakness (as shown) was assumed. The choice of the mesh assumes that about 10 m into the rock mass from the excavation surface elastic behaviour occurs. As the results of the analysis shows this is a reasonable assumption. The stope was excavated in stages by firing slices of approximately 2.5 m thickness. This was modelled by the program in four excavation stages by removing the appropriate Finite Elements from the mesh.

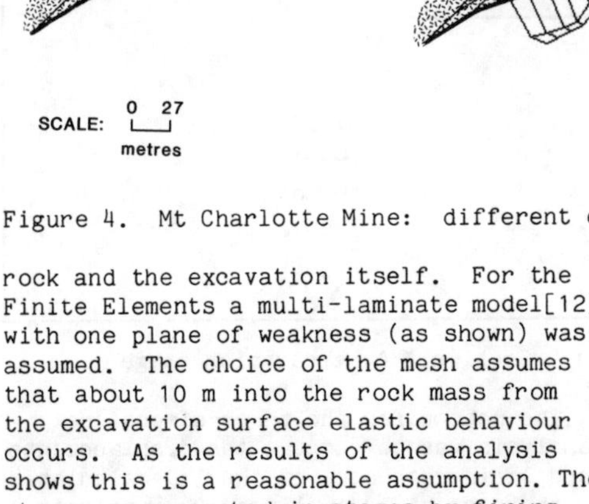

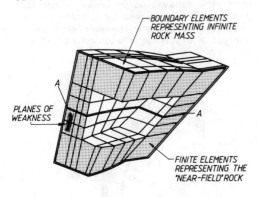

Figure 5. Cut-out mesh used for case study 3.

One of the results obtained is the dilation (loosening up) of the rock mass in the vicinity of the excavation, in particular in the hangingwall of the excavation.

Figure 6 shows contours of dilation on section A-A as predicted by the program for the last excavation stage.

Computing time for each excavation stage was 300 seconds on a CYBER 205 super-computer.

3.4 Case study 4: fully coupled analysis of a tunnel

The last case study relates to the three-dimensional analysis of a tunnel and to numerical studies of the stresses and displacements at the tunnel face[7]. The computer program FINAL[13], to which Sub-routines from program BEFE for computing the stiffness matrix of a B.E. region have been added, was used for the analysis.

The problem involves the sequential excavation of a tunnel with progressive installation of a shotcrete lining. The coupled mesh consists basically of four zones (Figure 7).

Zone A excavation region Zone B shotcrete Zone C nonlinear immediate region	Modelled by Finite Elements
Zone D elastic far region	Modelled by Boundary Elements

Zones A and C are modelled by 20-node brick elements and Zone B by 8-node thick

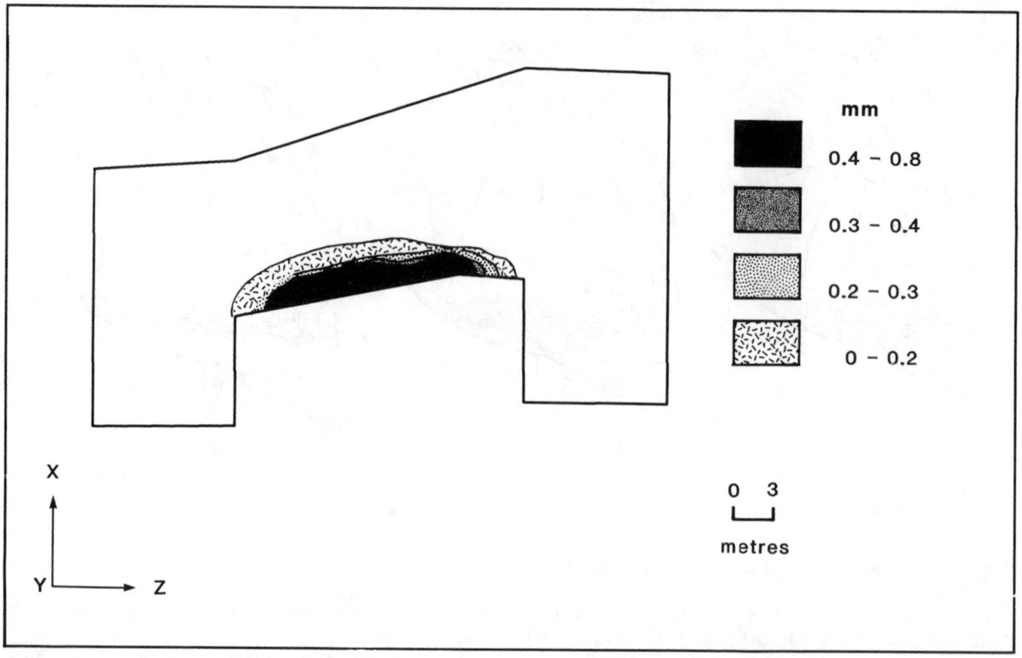

Figure 6. Contours of dilation on joint planes. Section A-A, excavation stage 4.

shell elements. The elastic far region is modelled by 8-node finite and 6-node infinite Boundary Elements.

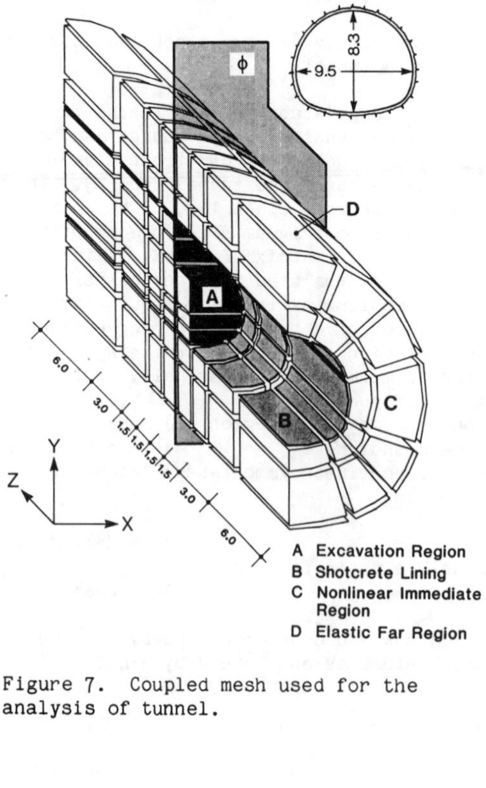

Figure 7. Coupled mesh used for the analysis of tunnel.

The reason for the three-dimensional analysis was to compare the displacements and lining stresses of the 3-D calculation with those of a simplified 2-D analysis using the stiffness reduction method.

In both the 2-D and 3-D analysis the actual excavation process is simulated by a step by step excavation. In the 2-D model the excavation progress in the third dimension is simulated by a stepwise reduction of the stiffness. For this purpose a stiffness reduction factor as described in [14] is used.

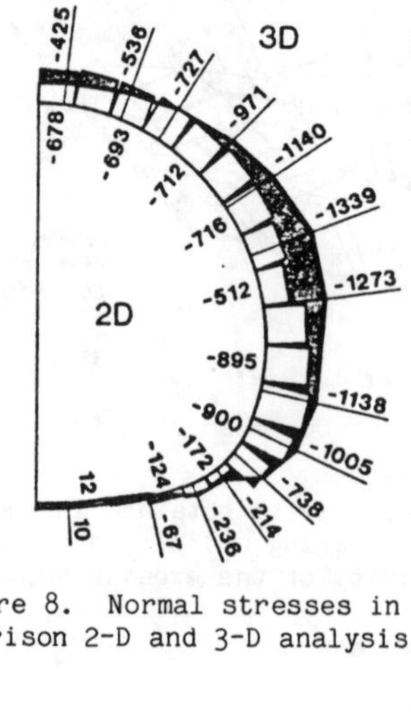

Figure 8. Normal stresses in lining: comparison 2-D and 3-D analysis.

Figure 8 shows that the lining stress distribution obtained from the 3-D analysis differs quite significantly from the simplified two-dimensional solution. This analysis exercise highlights the fact that near the tunnel face a true three-dimensional stress distribution prevails.

The analysis was performed on a VAX11/750 minicomputer. Computation times range from 4-6 hours with most of the time spent in solving for the unknowns at the interface with an out-of-core frontal solver. Further details are given in [15].

4 CONCLUSIONS

On case studies it has been shown how the Boundary Element Method and coupled method can be applied to the efficient three-dimensional stress analysis in geomechanics. All of the examples shown here require the consideration of the three-dimensional geometry and could not have been analysed using simplified plane-strain assumptions.

In the writer's opinion, the proposed analysis methods have put three-dimensional stress analysis of problems in rock and soil mechanics within the reach of the average mining or civil engineer. There is a dramatic improvement in user friendliness over other methods: times required to generate and input meshes are in the order of days rather than weeks or months and computing costs and times are reduced dramatically. Commercial costs of analysing a typical problem on a supercomputer via CSIRONET are in the range of $100 to $500 and computing times on an in-house mini or supermini computer are in the range of 1 to 3 hours.

In the future, efficient graphical preprocessors will cut the time required to specify a problem further. A major research project sponsored by AMIRA (Australian Mineral Industry Research Association) has recently commenced at CSIRO to develop graphical, workstation-based, preprocessors for defining problems in mining. This will be a joint venture with a team at the University of Innsbruck that has recently developed such preprocessors for use in tunnelling.

With this facility, three-dimensional stress analyses will become a routine design tool to the mining or civil engineer for feasibility and design studies and for "trouble-shooting" exercises.

ACKNOWLEDGMENTS
The permission of Z.C. Mine, Kalgoorlie Mining Associates and E.Z. Company/Rosebery Mine to publish some results of the modelling studies is sincerely acknowledged. The Rosebery mine simulation was carried out by Dr A Fourie with J.K.M.R.C. (Julius Kruttschnitt Mineral Research Centre). The meshes for the Mt Charlotte Mine were prepared by Max Lee of James Askew and Co, Melbourne under a collaborative agreement with CSIRO.

REFERENCES

[1] G.Beer and J.O.Watson, Introduction to Finite and Boundary Element Methods for Engineers, J. Wiley & Sons, (to appear in 1989)

[2] O.C.Zienkiewicz, D.W.Kelly and P.Bettess, "Marriage a la mode" Finite elements and boundary integrals, in Proc.Conf. Innovative Numerical Analysis in Engineering Science CETIM, Paris (1977)

[3] G.Beer, BEFE: Coupled Boundary Element - Finite Element Program, Structural Analysis Systems - 3, Niku-Lari ed., Pergamon Press, Oxford (1986)

[4] G.Beer, Implementation of Combined Boundary Element - Finite Element analysis with applications in geomechanics, Developments in Boundary Element Methods - 4, Banerjee and Watson eds, Applied Science, London 191-226 (1986)

[5] H.A.Mang, Z.Y.Chen, P.Torzicky, On the symmetricability of coupling matrices for BEM-FEM discretisations of solids, Proc. IUTAM Symp. on Advanced Boundary Element Methods: Applications in Solid and Fluid Mechanics, San Antonio, Texas, April 13-16, 1987

[6] H.A.Mang and Z.Y.Chen, Zur symmetrisier-barkeit von Kopplungsmatrizen bei BE-FE Diskretisierungen fester Körper ZAMM 67 (1987)

[7] G.Beer and G.Swoboda, Application of advanced boundary element and coupled methods in geomechanics, Proc. IUTAM Symp. on Advanced Boundary Element Methods: Applications in Solid and Fluid Mechanics, San Antonio, Texas, April 13-16, 1987

[8] G.Beer and J.O.Watson, Infinite Boundary Elements, Int.J.Num.Meth. Eng., in press.

[9] G.Beer, J.O.Watson and G.Swoboda, Three-dimensional analysis of tunnels using Infinite Boundary Elements, Computers & Geotechnics, 3, 37-38 (1987)

[10] G.Beer, Modelling different excavation strategies for lower lead lode at Z.C. Mine, Project Report No. 1, CSIRO Division of Geomechanics (1987)
[11] M.F.Lee, G.Beer, C.R.Windsor and J.Meneghini, The interaction of stopes, stresses and structure at the Mt Charlotte Mine, Western Australia - observations, numerical modelling and instrumentation, 2nd Int.Symp. on Rock Bursts and Seismicity in Mines, Univ. of Minnesota, USA, June 8-10 (1988)
[12] O.C.Zienkiewicz and G.N.Pande, Time dependent multi-laminate model of rocks - a numerical study of deformation and failure of rock masses, Int.J.Num. & Anal.Meth. in Geom., Vol. 1, 219-247.
[13] G.Swoboda, PROGRAMSYSTEM FINAL, Institut für Baustatik und Verstärkte Kunststoffe, University of Innsbruck, Austria (1984)
[14] G.Swoboda and G.Beer, Staedtischer Tunnelbau - Rechenmodelle und Resultatinterpretation als Grundlage fuer Planung un Bauausfuehrung. (Urban Tunnelling - Computational models as basis for design and construction). Finite Elemente - Anwendungen in der Baupraxis. Verlag Ernst Wilhelm und Sohn, Muenchen (1984)
[15] G.A.Swoboda, W.G.Mertz and G.Beer, Application of coupled FEM-BEM analysis for three-dimensional tunnel analysis,in Boundary Elements, Proc.Int.Conf., Beijing, Pergamon Press (1986)1

Numerical Methods in Geomechanics (Innsbruck 1988), Swoboda (ed.)
© 1989 Balkema, Rotterdam. ISBN 90 6191 809 X

Application of numerical analyses for tunnelling

H.Duddeck
Institut für Statik, Technische Universität Braunschweig, FR Germany

Abstract: The paper is the shorter version (e.g. without photos of the actual tunnelling work) of the introductory general lecture. In reviewing the application of numerical methods in tunnelling, the role is explained of the analysis within the entire design procedure of a tunnel project. Problems where numerical methods are essential are mentioned for soft ground tunnelling and for tunnels in rock. What has still to be done to meet expectations of the tunnelling engineers from conferences this? What kind of numerical methods are applied for the interpretation of field measurements? What are the achievements, what the shortcomings of the numerical methods?

1 THE ROLE OF STRUCTURAL MODELS

As soon as Homo erecturs some million years ago invented a digging tool, he dug a hole into the ground for the protection of his familiy. And it took thousands of years before later Homo sapiens arrived, who worried about whether the hole is a safe structure. Men have been successful tunnellers, long, long, many thousand years before the invention of numerical methods. Do tunnels need numerical methods? Do engineers, being ingenious, need finite and boundary-element-methods? Is the analysis of a tunnel an essential tool for providing safety and economy of a tunnel excavation? Or does a skilled miner perhaps rightly remark that the tunnel structure is safe not because of, but in spite of the numerical analysis?

Fig. 1 shows the overall design procedure as given by the recommendations of the Working Group of the International Tunnelling Association on structural design models /1/. The question, why we need models at all, is easily answered. Firstly: When we try to explain observed phenomena (say deformations at the tunnel crown), we have to analyse their causes. A theory is needed for the interpretation of observations, hence, a model of the structure and its behaviour. If the involved structure is as complex as the ground around a tunnel excavation and if the material behaves non-linearly, then only numerical methods are capable for solving the problem. Within the shown scheme of the design elements (Fig. 1), there are two places where numerical methods are applied:

- for the analysis by the mechanical model, from which we draw those criteria, which enable us to decide whether the design is safe or not, and

- for the interpretation of the field measurements.

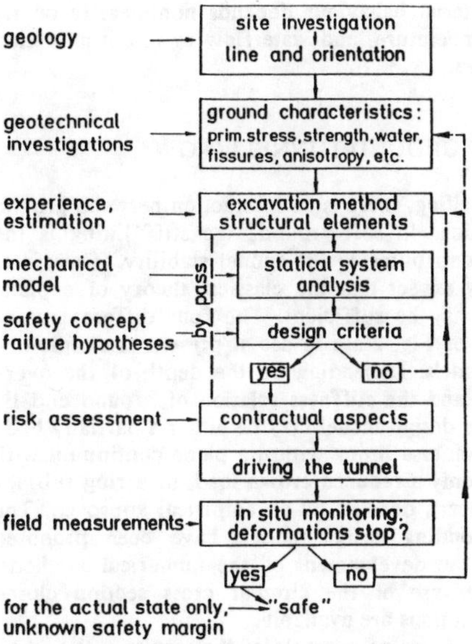

Fig. 1 Design procedure for tunnelling.

Secondly: We need models, too, for tendering. Hereby we have to predict, long before observations are possible, what kind of excavation procedure and support are appropriate for the special ground of the project. The model should cover the still to be experienced actual situations.

By further pondering upon models for tunnelling we may find that we need two kinds of structural desgin models. They differ in refinement. The more refined one should be as close as possible to reality

for explaining phenomena encountered in the field, for the interpretation of in-situ measurements, for back analysis.

The other structural design model for engineering design purposes may be a simpler one. It may not portray nature as it is, yet cover the actual tunnelling process, in most cases being on the safe side. The model may be reduced to few essential parameters in the same way as we are designing a building or a retaining wall by very simple approaches. Most of the models presented here at the conference will certainly belong to the first type. We hopefully expect that they nevertheless will contribute also to the simpler design models of the future.

Only by applying numerical methods to the design model we may gain more closiness to reality. The capacity of the numerical approaches is very large. The very complex geometry of an underground opening, especially of the changing geometry of the excavation phases requires an element-wise discretisation. A numerical analysis can cope with inhomogenities, fissure zones, faults, and strata of different ground, provided that geologists will tell us: where and what. In addition to this, numerical integration procedures are necessary, when the nonlinearities of ground, concrete, rock, rocksalt is considered, when the material behaviour depends nonlinearily on time, temperature, and waterflow as in consolidation problems.

2 SOFT GROUND TUNNELLING

In tunnelling, there is an interaction between ground and lining. In soft ground, the stiff lining is the main contributor to the tunnel stability. Therefore, we may expect that the classical theory of a plane model may be sufficient. The four different plane models of Fig. 2 are in use at present as simple design models. Depending on the depth of the overburden and the stiffness relation of ground and lining the design model may be either a partially bedded beam or a lining within a plane continuum with full or only a reduced crown load, or a ring subjected to loads derived by an empirical approach. The corresponding design models have been proposed before the development of the numerical methods. And because of the circular cross section closed form solutions are available.

Fig. 3 shows an example of the results obtained by applying the models (1) or (2) of Fig. 2. Some results for the bending moments at the crown are presented.It also shows the limit of what anlytical solutions are achieving.

Fig. 4 demonstrates how far reality may deviate from theory. The three adjacent lines of the Elbe-Tunnel have been driven by a shield. The lines are measurement results. The hoop forces should be almost constant along the lining. The bending moments deviate even by the plusminus sign form theoretical predictions. By more scrutinized investigations it turned out that the erection of the segments and the consecutive driving of the adjacent

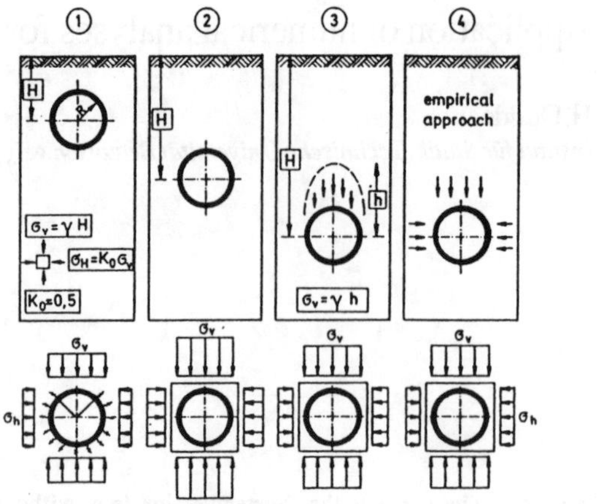

Fig. 2 Four different plane models /1/.

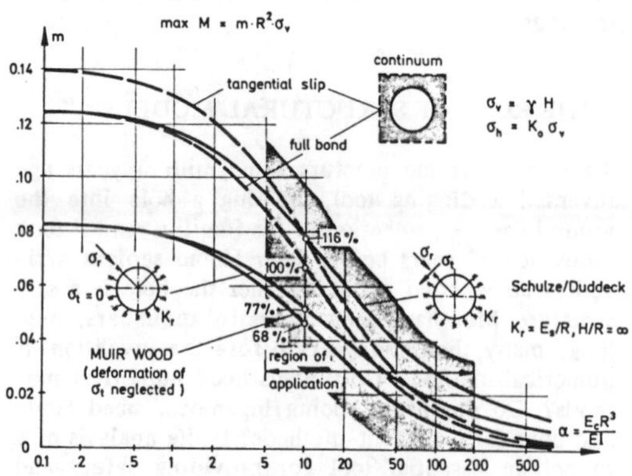

Fig. 3 Maximum moment at the crown for different plane models, plotted over stiffness relation of ground E_c and linging EJ /2/.

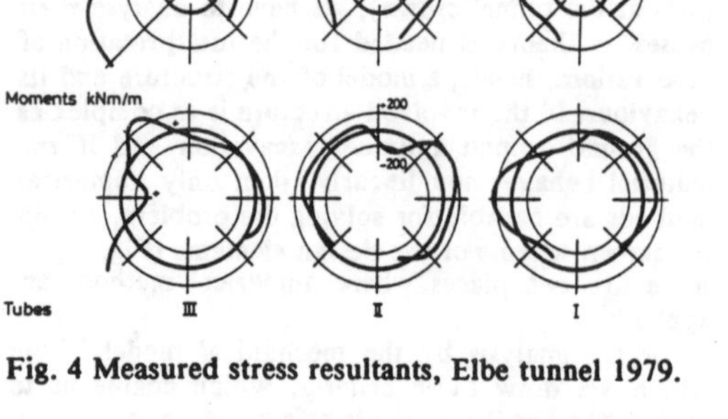

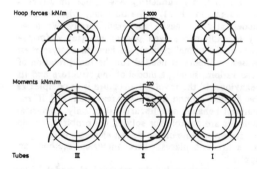

Fig. 4 Measured stress resultants, Elbe tunnel 1979.

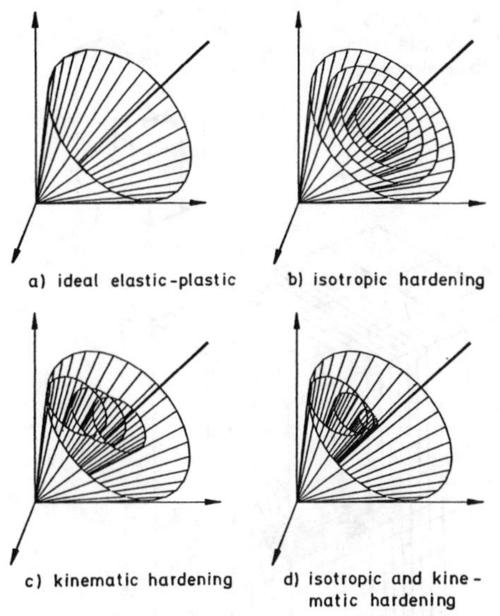

Fig. 5 Yield surfaces for sand (without caps) /3/.

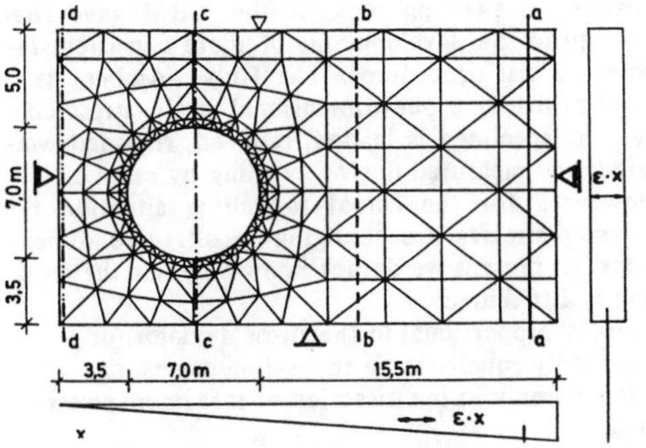

Fig. 6 Induced strains by mining subsidence /4/.

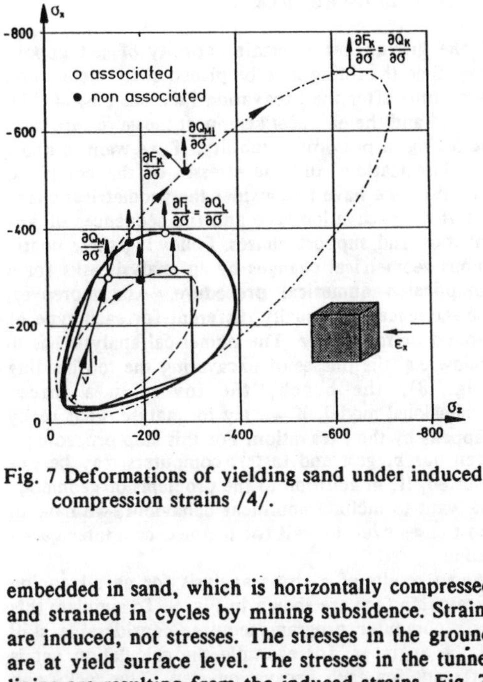

Fig. 7 Deformations of yielding sand under induced compression strains /4/.

lines are of considerable influence. So, even in the field of classical tunnelling we need more complex approaches.

There are still problems of shielddriven tunnelling where the application of advanced numerical methods may be appropriate. For the investigation of the stability of the tunnel face we still have to develop consistent models. Only by numerical models may we succeed to cover the different failure modes at the face for cohesionless sand or for overconsolidated clay. How is the stability affected by pore water pressure and consolidation, especially by shield chamber supports of bentonite, slurry or air pressure? Advanced numerical analyses may also be helpful in solving the more complex interactions between ground and lining as for example in the case

- of ground improvements by grouting,
- by extruded concrete,
- or in the case of tunnel pipe jacking, where a boundary layer of ground is overstressed.

For a more consistent approach to soft ground behaviour we need more realistic stress-strain laws and yield surfaces for soil, as those shown in Fig. 5 for sand. By the moving inner cones the behaviour under cyclic loadings may be covered. The caps for the cones are not shown here. Similar constitutive equations may also be applied for other types of ground, as for example for clay. When our geotechnical problem is kept in a horizontal plane of the stress space then the very significant deviations of different approaches are evident, see Fig. 7.

Fig. 6 is an example in which for tunnels the correct determination of deformations are important. The tunnel for the subway lines in Gelsenkirchen is embedded in sand, which is horizontally compressed and strained in cycles by mining subsidence. Strains are induced, not stresses. The stresses in the ground are at yield surface level. The stresses in the tunnel lining are resulting from the induced strains, Fig. 7. Therefore the design values for the tunnel lining differ dramatically with the assumptions of the ground, as those for associated or non-associated deformations laws, kinematic hardening and softening. Here simpler approaches are definitely wrong.

Freezing soft ground for tunnelling, is an other problem where we have to apply numerical methods because of non-linear behaviour. Freezing the ground asks for time and temperature dependent stress-strain laws, volumetrical increase, determination of heave at the surface, shotcrete creep at low temperature, effects of interval freezing.

For swelling ground, either chemically induced as for anhydrite or physically as for clay, we still need adequate constitutive laws. The international commission on swelling rock of the ISRM gave first priority to the developments of more consistent laboratory test procedures. The Huber-Amberg tests yield primarily a one-dimensional strain-stress curve. The specimen is loaded, relieved, reloaded, watered, and measured during swelling by relieve. However, for the actual tunnelling situation the primary stresses are changing in all three dimensions. At present we do not know whether the swelling is distributed:

- firstly proportional to the stress deviator, or
- secondly equally in all three dimensions, or
- thirdly only in the direction of maximum stress release.

If we want to know whether swelling may cause collapse of a tunnel: only numerical methods will provide answers.

3 TUNNELLING IN ROCK

If the ground has a certain capacity of selfsupporting, then the lining may be placed some meters and some time after the excavation face has passed. The ground and the engineer's support measures are participating in providing stability. If we want to know the deformations and the stresses of the combined structure, we have to consider the geometrical changes at the excavation face and the sequences of excavation and support phases. Following these continuous geometrical changes by an analysis asks for a complicated numerical procedure. And moreover, the sequences are usually different for each type of ground or rock layer. The numerical analysis has to follow e.g. the phases of excavating the top heading (Fig. 8), the bench, the invert in a three-dimensional model, if we try to analyse what really happens by the excavation. For this step procedure even our biggest and fastest computers may be exhausted. If, in addition to the problems of geometry, we want to include nonlinear behaviour, we have in most cases even to wait for the next computer generation.

Some results of a stress analysis for an advancing excavation face are shown in Fig. 9. To simulate this by a computer program requires considerable skill of the engineer, for example the calculation net is different for each excavation step. The rock, and hence the tunnel may fail either by too large a stress or - most often - by stress release at the tunnel face. Non-uniform stress release results in a greater stress deviator.

During the last years the application of the boundary-element-method to tunnelling problems has been further developed, so that this method may be applied in engineering practice as a complementary tool to the finite-element-method. In tunnelling we may profit from each of the specific advantages. The region with distinct non-linear behaviour is better be simulated by finite-elements. The outer region up to infinity may better be represented by boundary-elements, Fig. 11. Thus, we avoid problems at the outer boundaries for the finite-

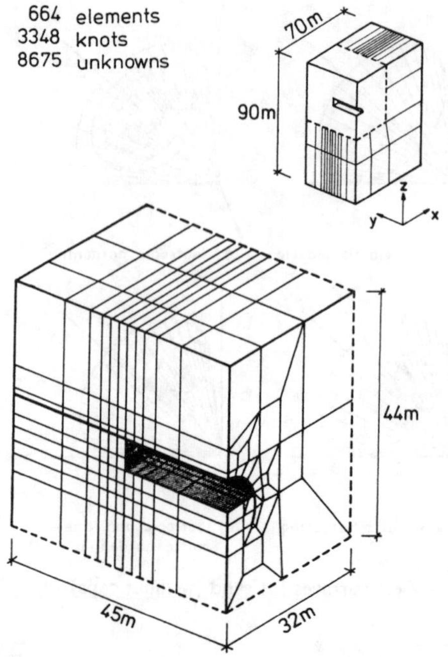

Fig. 8 Three-dimensional FEM model for the analysis of the top heading excavation.

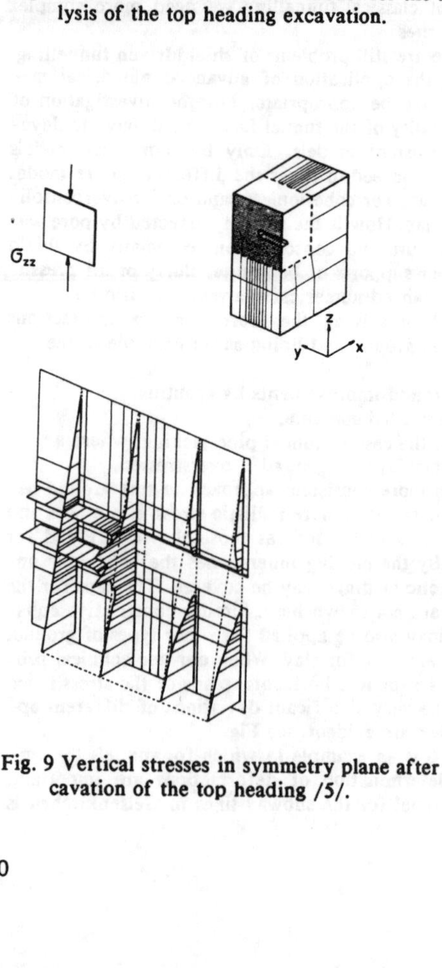

Fig. 9 Vertical stresses in symmetry plane after excavation of the top heading /5/.

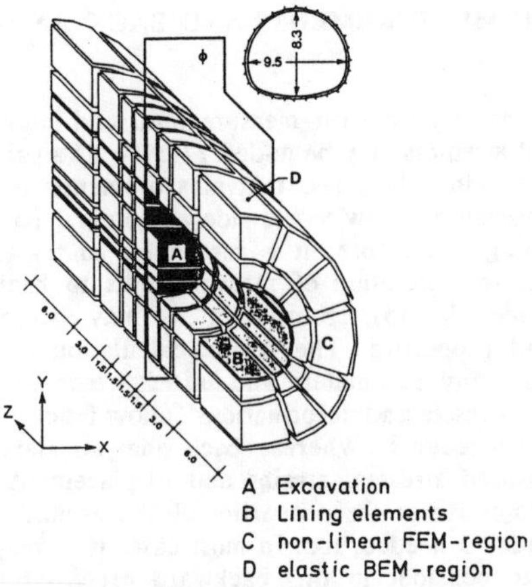

Fig. 10 Coupled FEM- and BEM-Regions by Swoboda /6/.

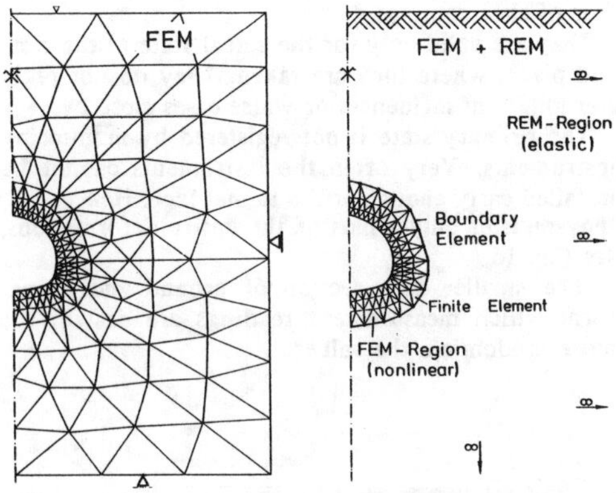

Fig. 11

element-method. If the boundary-element region can be taken as elastic, then the solutions are especially simple. Fig. 10 shows the three-dimensional application of coupled finite- and boundary-elements for an advancing tunnel excavation by Swoboda and Mertz /6/.

The application of numerical analyses for nonlinear rock behaviour has become a standard engineering technique, especially when the problem can be reduced to one of a plane system. Fig. 12 shows an example in mining. Here the question is, whether the pillars between galleries are endangered when linings for the galleries are not provided. A graphic display (of course: in colours and not in black and white as here) can visualize for example the regions of different rates of plastification around the three galleries.

In mining and in excavating caverns, there are many problems which still defy any numerical analysis. Mining engineers may ask us whether a numerical analysis can be of any help to decide that the pillars and ceilings and the mining area at whole are designed with appropriate safety. Considering the three-dimensional approach necessary, the manyfold excavation phases, the temperature and creep effects, the variable compactness of the supporting back fill, we would honestly say: no, or: not yet. We need much more computer capacity than available at present. We do need also correct stress-strain-time-temperature-relations, for example for the back fill, and we do need perhaps also the manpower for programming.

Fig. 13 presents the calculation models of a tunnel struck by a sinkhole either at the invert or close beside the tunnel. Compared to the mine the three-dimensional sinkhole problem is much closer within reach of our present capacity of numerical methods.

In Fig. 14 the almost classical Fenner-Pacher characteristics are given, to comment on the objectives of thus conference. These curves of the convergence of the ground and the resistence of the lining have been invented in Austria. Many tunnellers are using them as design tools. They are very useful for Professors to explain students what happens between ground and lining. However, they do not meet somewhat higher demands, since they are valid only for circular cross sections and are considering only one parameter (the constant inward deformation). Therefore, we have to overcome this oversimplified approach. By advanced numerical methods we should be able to consider the stress release at the excavation face and the gradual reaction of the lining and other support measures within a more comprehensive approach. Yet, there are still many problems to struggle with, even for the advaced numerical methods offered at present:

1. Rock is not a continuum, but a jointed discontinuum, very often brocken in many directions and with distinctly oriented strength and failure surfaces. All the element methods are basically continuum-methods of homogenious media. So, we have to encourage all efforts which develop analyses of discontinua, like those by Goodman, Cundall, Fairhurst and all those presenting papers on this subject here in Innsbruck, as Desai and Kawamoto.

2. The simulation of the sequences of excavation and support measures should cover numerically also more complicated cases, as that e.g. where two smaller bench-tunnels are driven prior to the main excavation of the crown heading.

3. We still have to work on deriving consistent models which cover correctly the effect of rock bolting, the development of shotcrete strength, its creep properties at early time.

4. Experienced tunnellers know that ground water can be a vicious enemy, contributing to the softening of strength and friction. Ho do we include these effects in our constitutive equations?

5. It is much easier to investigate for example stress-strain fields of stable situations. But what we

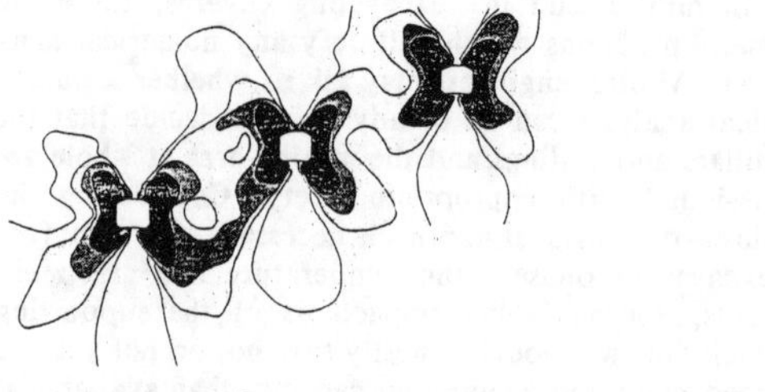

Fig. 12 Application to mining, stresses around three galleries.

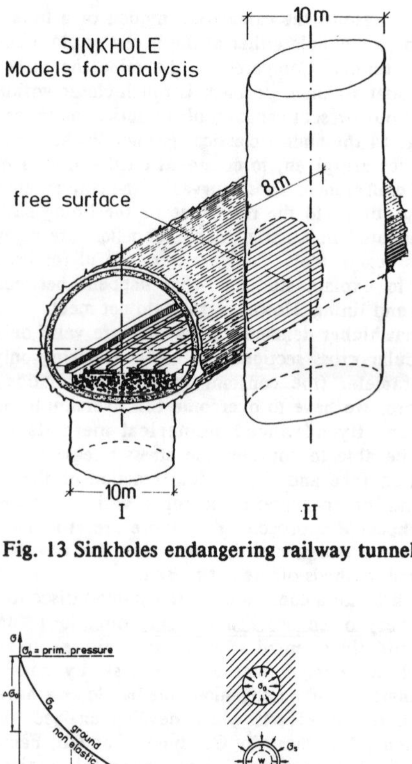

Fig. 13 Sinkholes endangering railway tunnel.

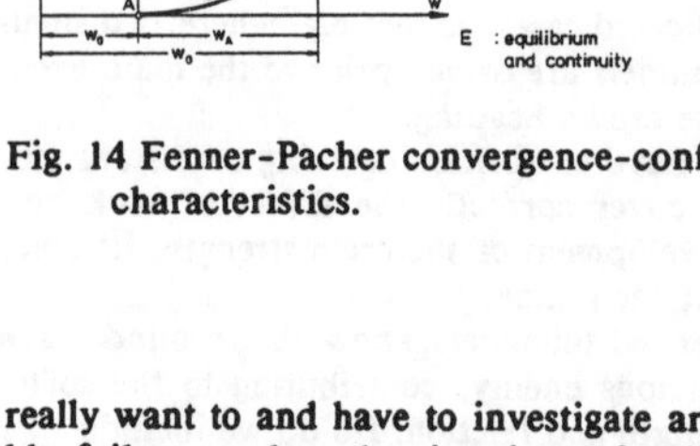

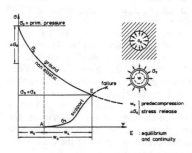

Fig. 14 Fenner-Pacher convergence-confinement characteristics.

really want to and have to investigate are the possible failure modes, the situations of collapsing tunnels. If we can predict by analysis how far off an in-situ situation is of collapsing, only then reliable safety margins may be defined.

4 IN-SITU MEASUREMENTS AND BACK ANALYSIS

Some comments on in-situ-measurements and interpretational attempts may be added /7/. We owe primarily Austrian colleagues, that measurements during excavation are now worldwide an integral part of tunnelling. Therefore, it is reasonable to try to extend the interpretation of measurements to back analyses (see Fig. 15), from which we may extract the ground properties. The design calculation can cope with many parameters and unrestricted nonlinearities. Stresses and deformations follow from integration procedures. Whereas back analysis starts from measured stresses, strains and displacements. In order to arrive at the properties of the ground a design model is needed, too. In most cases it is very difficult to consider in this backward process the nonlinearities. Furthermore, the displacements are integrals of a manifold of influences and probabilistic values. Therefore, methods for minimizing the errors have to be added. In view of the emphasis in numerical approaches given to back analyses, it is worthwile to point out that measurements are not free of shortcomings:

- They are valid only for the actual state at the time and place, where they are taken. They do not register longterm influences or worse cases close by.
- The primary state is not registered by monitoring instruments. Very often the instruments cannot be installed early enough at the tunnel face. Hence, they register only a part of the entire deformations, see Fig. 16.
- The smaller the section of ground and lining, form which measurement readings are drawn, the more random are the values.

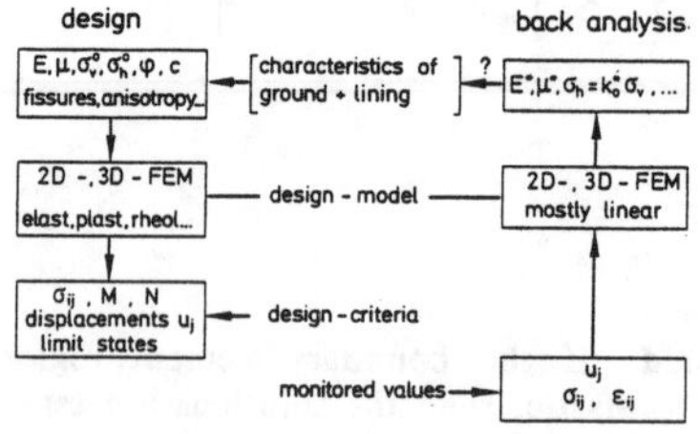

Fig. 15 Design versus back analysis.

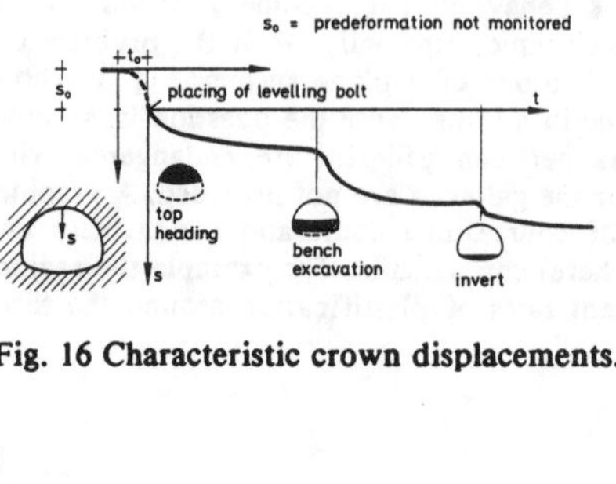

Fig. 16 Characteristic crown displacements.

- The integral character of the measured deformations does not allow to analyse directly from measurements the causes of a deformation, all the factors which contribute to it.
- Measurements are not available for planning and tendering.
- Measurements are not repeatable, hence, errors are concealed.

If this is so, then also a back analysis is effected by all these deficits.

5 FAILURE MODES AND CONCLUDING REMARKS

The concluding topic is returning to the overall objective of numerical methods in geomechanics. The methods of analyses should provide the engineer for his design and field work with a consistent, simple, yet accurate enough method, by which criteria may be drawn that enable him to decide whether a structure is safe. These criteria may be by definition (see Fig. 17): failure of a point, if limits of stresses are applied, or development of plastic zones, or collaps of the system. The definitions for loss of serviceability or for failure can be very different as:
- loosing watertightness,
- durability not secured,
- deformations too large,
- strength locally exhausted,
- damages due to strength failure,
- collapse of system.

Real tunnel very often fail quite differently than expected by analysis (Fig. 18). Was exceeding some given limits of stress the cause of these failures? Loss of friction? The inappropriate excavation method? Does our theory and our numerical method include cases of rock, which dissolves into a fluid ground?

Failures in the ground have in most cases the character of kinematic modes which move along geometrically possible yielding fracture surfaces. The character of a continuum which obeys stress-strain laws, is completely lost. Most often water plays an important role. Do our mathematical and mechanical models cover these failure cases? Are they able to predict that danger of a sudden collaps is close at hand, although measurements do not indicate any danger?

There is no doubt, that we do need structural models for our engineering structures and that we do need methods, numerical methods for analysis. As any good theory has to accomplish, we want to predict how the real structure will behave. Sometimes we have to analyse afterwards why a structure failed. Structures in the ground are very complicated. In spite of all the achievements, there is still very much to do in the field of numerical methods in order to close the gap between real ground behaviour and our present approaches.

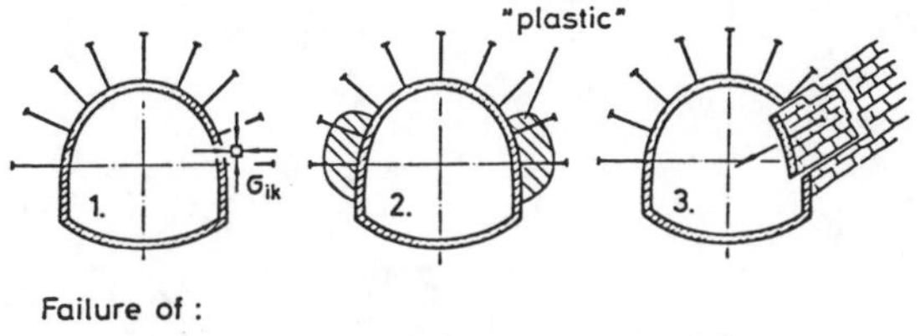

Fig. 17 Different safety concepts.

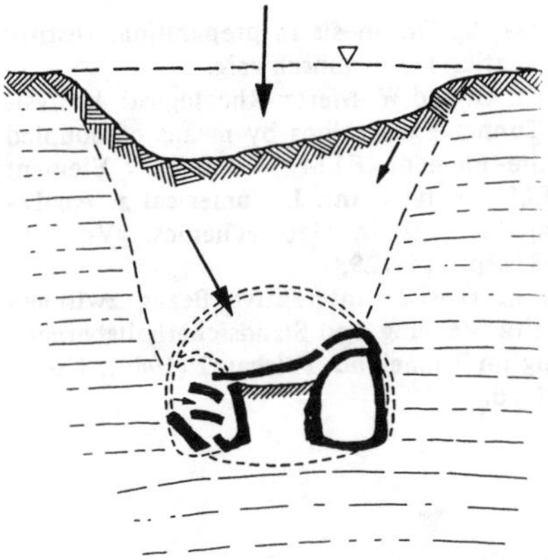

Fig. 18 Tunnel collapse of preliminary lining.

REFERENCES

/1/ Guidelines for the Design of Tunnels. ITA working group on General Approaches to the Design of Tunnels. Tunnelling and Underground Space Technology, Pergamon Press, August 1988.

/2/ Duddeck, H. and J. Erdmann: On Structural Design Models for Tunnels in Soft Soil. Underground Space, Vol. 9 (1985) p. 246-259.

/3/ Winselmann, D.: Stoffgesetze mit isotroper und kinematischer Verfestigung sowie deren Anwendung auf Sand. Bericht Nr. 84-44 aus dem Institut für Statik der TU Braunschweig, 1984, see also Proc. 6. Int. Conf. Numerical Methods in Geomechanics. Innsbruck 1988, p. 403-413.

/4/ Ahrens, H. and D. Winselmann: Berechnung von Tunneln im Sand bei bergbaulichen Zwangsverformungen. Finite-Element-Anwendungen in der Baupraxis. Bochum 1988, Verlag Ernst u. Sohn, Berlin (in Preparation)

/5/ Kielbassa, S.: Dr. thesis in preparation. Institut für Statik, TU Braunschweig.
/6/ Swoboda, G. and W. Mertz: Rheological Analysis of Tunnel Excavations by means of coupled Finite-Element (FEM) - Boundary Element (BEM) Analysis. Int. J. Numerical a. Analytical Methods in Geomechanics. Vol. 11 (1987), p. 115-129.
/7/ Duddeck, H.: Der interaktive Bezug zwischen in-situ Messung und Standsicherheitsberechnung im Tunnelbau. Felsbau 2 (1984), No. 1, p. 8-16.

Late papers

Numerical Methods in Geomechanics (Innsbruck 1988), Swoboda (ed.)
© 1989 Balkema, Rotterdam. ISBN 90 6191 809 X

Identification of constitutive parameters of soil using pressuremeter test

Tadanobu Sato & Toru Shibata
Disaster Prevention Research Institute, Kyoto University, Uji, Kyoto, Japan

Yoshio Hirai
Takenaka Technical Research Laboratory, Minamikawachi, Osaka, Japan

ABSTRACT: A practical method has been developed to identify the in-situ values of material parameters in a constitutive equation of soil. All constitutive parameters are identified from a simple conventional pressuremeter test result. Powell's method for minimizing a function of several variables without calculating derivatives is applied to identify constitutive parameters. The finite element method is used to analyze the deformation field surrounding the probe of pressuremeter. The method to evaluate the stability of identified parameters was also proposed through the eigen value analysis of the resolution matrix.

1 INTRODUCTION

Several different types of field and laboratory tests are required to define parameters in a constitutive equation of soil. The method we here have developed, however, needs only one pressuremeter test result. We modified a system identification technique which was proposed in the field of automatic control [1]. Parameter identification consists of modeling the constitutive law and optimizing it. Once constitutive parameters that characterize soil behavior have been defined, identification is easily made by minimizing the square error with respect to each parameter. The actual constitutive law, however, has a complicated structure such that even simple modeling is difficult. The other method is the phenomenological approximation of constitutive law by fitting a mathematical formula to the relation between the input and output of system. The linear and/or nonlinear least square method and the maximum likelihood method are the basic tools used to identify constitutive parameters.

The fundamental concept of the method is to regard observed volume change of the probe in the pressuremeter as an output from an experimental filter and calculated volume change as an output from a theoretical filter. Optimum values of constitutive parameters can be obtained by minimizing the difference between outputs from those two filters [2]. The finite element analysis was used to simulate volume change of the probe and a deformation field of sand surrounding the pressuremeter.

We applied the developed method to a constitutive equation of sand including the effect of stress-dilatancy. A pressuremeter test result was used to verify the method. To evaluate accuracy and mutual correlations among the identified parameters, sensitivity analysis was performed.

2 THEORETICAL FRAME

Least square method is adopted for optimizing an objective function. The constitutive equation of soil has non-linear form and hence it is necessary to minimize a non-linear objective function. The objective function S is selected as the residual error between the observed values and estimated values of volume change of the probe.

Generally, a constitutive equation can be expressed by the form

$$d\varepsilon_{ij} = h\frac{\partial g}{\partial \sigma_{ij}}\,df = d\varepsilon_{ij}(\sigma_{ij},\ d\sigma_{ij},\ \gamma_k) \qquad (k=1,2,\cdots,L) \tag{1}$$

in which, $d\varepsilon_{ij}$ is the strain increment tensor, h the hardening function, g the plastic potential function, σ_{ij} the stress tensor, $d\sigma_{ij}$ the stress increment tensor, f is yield function, ν_k are soil parameters which define the constitutive equation, and L is the number of parameters.

Although Eq.(1) is the constitutive equation using non-associated flow rule, the following discussions are valid for any kind of constitutive relationship if the strain increment can be expressed in terms of constitutive parameters.

In the finite element method using the constitutive Eq.(1), the relation between nodal displacement increment vector {du} and nodal force increment vector {dF} can be expressed as follows:

$$\{dF\} = [K]\{du\} \quad (2) \qquad \{d\varepsilon\} = [B]\{du\} \quad (3)$$

$$\{d\sigma\} = [D]\{d\varepsilon\} \quad (4)$$

in which, $\{d\varepsilon\}$ is the element strain increment vector, $\{d\sigma\}$ the element stress increment vector, [B] strain matrix, and [D] stress matrix defined from the constitutive relationship.

Eq.(3) is the relationship between strain and displacement. Eq.(4) is the constitutive equation expressed in a strain increment vector space. Component of matrix [D] are function of soil parameters ν_k.

If we denote u_i and $\tilde{u}_i$ as the observed and estimated values of displacement at the probe surface, the square error between them can be expressed as follows:

$$S = \sum_{i=1}^{n} (u_i - \tilde{u}_i)^2 \qquad (5)$$

in which, n is the number of experimental data. The optimum values of the soil parameters in the constitutive equation can be obtained by minimizing the value of S.

Using Eqs.(1) and (3), the displacement is expressed as a non-linear function of soil parameters. The linearization, therefore, must be done with respect to the soil parameters at the vicinity of the first approximation of the parameters ν_k^0 as follows:

$$u_i = u_i(\nu_k^0) + \frac{\partial (u_i)}{\partial \nu_K}\bigg|_{\nu=\nu_k^0} (\hat{\nu}_k - \nu_k^0) \qquad (6)$$

in which $\hat{\nu}_k$ is the second approximation of soil parameters.

The condition to minimize S gives

$$\frac{\partial}{\partial \nu_k}(u_i - \tilde{u}_i)^2 = 0 \qquad (u_i = \Sigma du_i) \qquad (7)$$

The normal equation is obtained by substituting Eq.(6) into Eq.(7) and performing the differentiation.

$$(\hat{\nu}_k - \nu_k^0) \frac{\partial (u_i)}{\partial \nu_k}\bigg|_{\nu_k=\nu_k^0} \frac{\partial (u_i)}{\partial \nu_l}\bigg|_{\nu_l=\nu_l^0} = (u_i - \tilde{u}_i) \frac{\partial (u_i)}{\partial \nu_l}\bigg|_{\nu_l=\nu_l^0} \qquad (8)$$

Eq.(8) is a simultaneous equation with the degree equal to the number of unknown parameters, and hence the values of $\hat{\nu}_k - \nu_k^0$ are obtained.

Eq.(8) was obtained by linearizing a non-linear equation using Taylor's expansion. Its solution is, therefore, sometimes very unstable according to the initial values of the constitutive parameters. To overcome this difficulty, minimization of Eq.(5) was directly performed using Powell's second procedure [3,4]. A component of the coefficient matrix of normal equation $\partial u_i/\partial \nu_k \cdot \partial u_i/\partial \nu_l$ can be calculated numerically once the optimum solutions are given.

This coefficient matrix is called the resolution matrix [5] and used for the sensitivity analysis of the constitutive parameters. Let the vector space defined by the increment of parameters to be m and that defined by the difference between observed and calculated displacement to be d, then the following expression is obtained from Eq.(8)

$$G^T G m = G^T d \qquad (9)$$

A component of matrix G is given by

$$G_{ij} = \frac{\partial (u_i)}{\partial \nu_k}\bigg|_{\nu_k=\hat{\nu}_k} \qquad (10)$$

in which $\hat{\nu}_k$ is the optimum value of constitutive parameters.

Considering eigen values of the resolution matrix G^TG, the sensitivity of identified parameter is evaluated. Let λ_n and $\bar{m}_n$ to be eigen value and eigen vector. Eq.(9) can be rewritten in the eigen space as follows:

$$\lambda_n \bar{m}_n = \bar{d}_n \;, \quad \bar{m}_n = \phi_n^T m \;, \quad \bar{d}_n = \phi_n^T G^T d \qquad (11)$$

Eq.(11) expresses influence of the displacement error on the error of identified parameter, because values of $\bar{d}_n$ and $\bar{m}_n$ are measure of both errors in the eigen space. If the eigen value is large, the accuracy of identification is high because even a large error of displacement results in a small error of soil parameter. However for the estimated displacement using identified parameters, small change of the corresponding parameter leads to a large error of estimated displacement. Hence, eigen values of the resolution matrix can be used as sensitivity measures of the constitutive parameters. Eigen vectors are used to evaluate appropriateness of selecting constitutive parameters.

We chose Nishi model [5] as the constitutive equation. The constitutive parameters are Young's modulus (E), the stress ratio ($\eta=\tau_{oct}/\sigma_m$) at failure (Mf), the stress ratio at the maximum volume contraction state (Mm), the initial tangent modulus of $\eta-\gamma_{oct}$ curve (G), the slope of virgin compression line (λ), and the coefficient of earth pressure at rest (Ko). Poisson's ratio ν is not included in the constitutive parameters because there is no term appearing E and ν independently in the components of stiffness matrix [D] of Eq.(4).

3 ELEMENT COLLOCATION

We use quadratic isoparametric elements to simulate the deformation field around the probe of pressuremeter. First we investigate the influence of element collocation on the calculated values. It is sufficient to consider only a quadrant of the deformation field because of the symmetry of the system to simulate the pressuremeter test in the chamber. We divide this quadrant into 4,9,16,25 and 30 elements respectively. Fig.1 shows the distributions of nodes along the X-axis. We distinguish element (or mesh) collocation by the number indicated in Fig.1.

Fig.2 shows the result analyzed using the mesh of No.1,3,4 and 6. The values of parameters used in analysis are shown in the figure. We assume that the pressuremeter test begins at isotropic consolidation state with a pressure of $0.2kgf/cm^2$. The ordinate is the internal pressure and the abscissa is the circumferential strain (u/r). The internal pressure is increased up to $1.2kgf/cm^2$ by applying ten steps of pressure increment of $0.1kgf/cm^2$.

The radial displacement at the outer edge of analyzing field is fixed. Therefore the nodal displacement at the probe surface is strongly affected by this boundary condition when the number of elements is not sufficient. As the number of elements increases the effect of boundary condition decreases and the circumferential strain (u/r) approaches to a certain value.

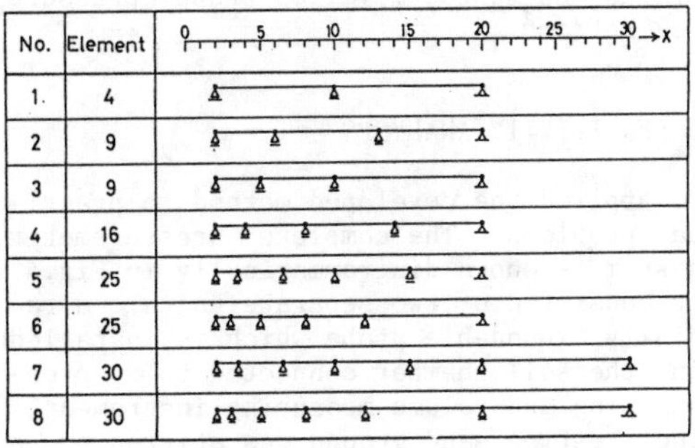
No.
Element
0 5 10 15 20 25 30 →X
1 4
2 9
3 9
4 16
5 25
6 25
7 30
8 30

Fig.1 Distributions of nodes along the X-axis.

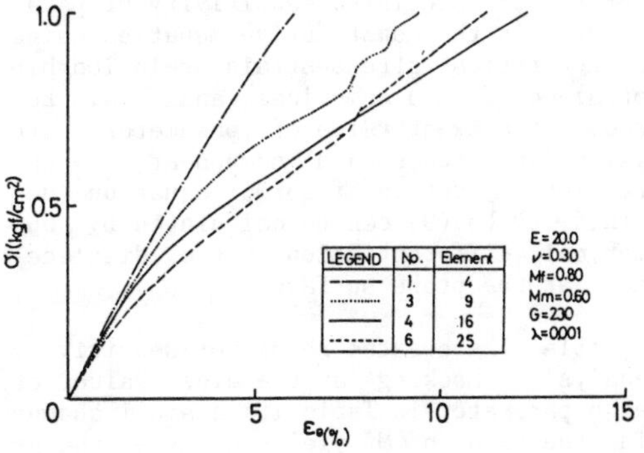

Fig.2 Calculated stress-strain relationship.

For the case of No.6 (25 elements), the pattern of deformation becomes abnormal when the internal pressure is beyond $0.4kgf/cm^2$. The reason for this effect can be classified into the following two cases: The first case is that the applied pressure increment in analysis is too large and the second case is that the mesh collocation is not appropriate. First we investigate the effect of the applied pressure increment on the stress-strain relationship and it can be concluded that there is no effect if the applied pressure increment is less than 0.1kgf/cm^2. Three pairs of simulated stress-strain relationships are shown in Fig.3 in order to investigate the effect of mesh collocation. Each pair was obtained using mesh with same number of elements but different collocation. If the number of element in the analyzing field exceeds 25 the stress-strain relationship becomes very stable up to the level of probe pressure 0.7 kgf/cm^2.

4 SENSITIVITY ANALYSES

We applied the developed method to practical problems. The complete pressuremeter system is shown diagrammatically in Fig.4. It consisted of two separate units: a radially expandable probe which is installed in the soil chamber connected to a pressurizing and volume measuring instrument. The testing sand ground was stirred by a water-jet supplying from the bottom of the soil chamber. After the ground hmogenized a overburden pressure was applied through the rubber balloon rested on the testing ground.

First we calculated sensitivity of parameters in the constitutive equation using a theoretical stress-strain relationship obtained from a numerical analysis. Because the exact value of parameters are given and hence each component of the resolution matrix of normal equation defined by Eq.(9) can be calculated by numerical differentiation of the displacement at the probe surface.

Table 1 shows the result of sensitivity analysis. Looking at the eigen value of each parameter in Table 1, a small change in the value of Mf yields a large change

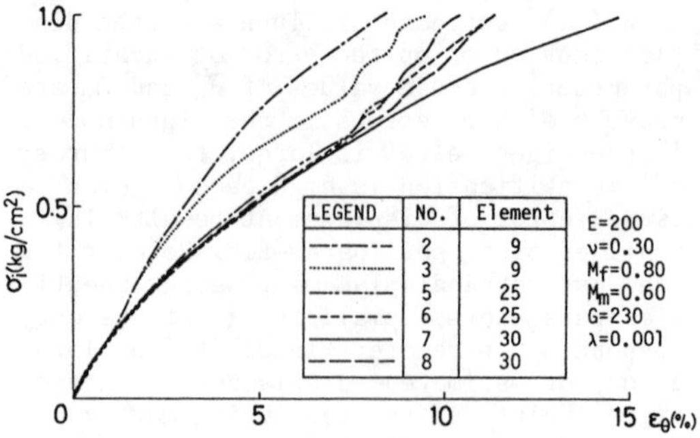

Fig.3 The effect of mesh collocation on stress-strain relationships.

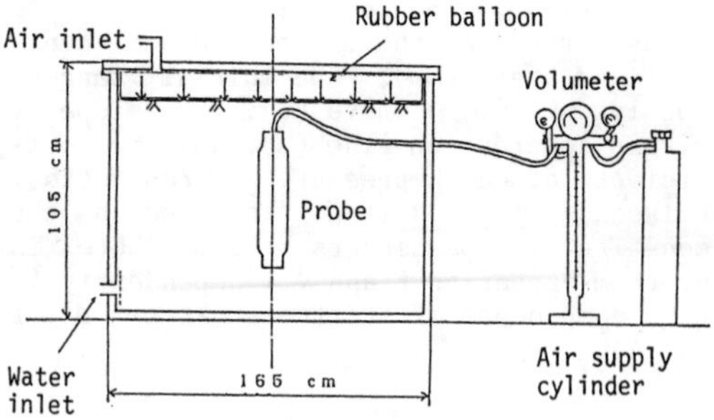

Fig.4 Pressuremeter test apparatus.

of displacement increment because the eigen value of Mf has the largest value in the parameters. The eigen values of parameters becomes smaller in the order of Mf, Mm, G, ,E and Ko. The effect of small

Table 1 Calculated sensitivity of constitutive parameters using simulated probe pressure and deformation

Eigen value	Mfx 10^7	Mmx 10^3	G	λ x10^{-1}	Ex 10^{-1}	Kox 10^{-4}
	0.105	0.669	0.883	0.376	0.147	0.598
Eigen vector	-0.0009	-0.6223	0.7527	-0.0223	-0.2778	0.0029
	0.0006	-0.7107	-0.6579	-0.0399	-0.3080	0.0055
	0.0000	0.3235	0.0147	0.0005	0.4329	0.9990*
	-0.9999*	-0.0004	-0.0019	-0.0004	0.0001	0.0000
	0.0132	-0.0425	-0.0095	0.9989*	-0.0201	0.0000
	-0.0004	-0.0303	-0.0198	-0.0017	-0.8000*	0.0442

change of the parameter on the displacement increment decreases in the order of Mf, Mm, G, λ, E and K_o. When observed displacement increment is given, the value of parameter with small eigen value results in a large change of identifying parameter. Therefore parameters such as K_σ, E, and λ should be determined by using data obtained from different test conditions because the accuracy of identified parameter is not guaranteed for the parameters with small eigen values.

In eigen vectors of Mf, Mm, E and Ko we can see one component with large absolute value and the other components with very small values, but there are more than two components with large absolute values in eigen vectors of Mm and G. This means that there is an interaction between Mm and G, and coupling of mode between them occurs. This coupling of mode between Mm and G is peculiar to the deformation field of pressuremeter test. The reason occurring this phenomena becomes clear through the application of sensitivity analysis to triaxial test results.

5 IDENTIFICATION OF CONSTITUTIVE PARAMETERS USING PRESSURE METER TEST RESULTS

Fig.5 shows the calculated stress-strain relationship using optimum values of the constitutive parameters. These parameters were identified using pressuremeter test result under the condition of overburden pressure to be 0.5kgf/cm^2. The solid line in Fig.5 is the calculated stress-strain relationship and the marks (o) are experimental results. In Fig.5, initial values of the constitutive parameters and identified values at the final step of iteration are also shown. Because the constitutive law is expressed in terms of stress ratio, all constitutive parameters have dimensionless quantity. It can be seen from this figure that the experimental result can be explained by the theoretical solution obtained using optimum values of constitutive parameters.

Table 2 shows eigen values and eigen vectors of parameters which were identified using the pressuremeter test results. Looking at the eigen values of each parameter in Table 2, the eigen value of parameter Mf has the highest value. Because small change of measured displacement dose not affect the value of Mf, in other word, data being used for identification must be reliable. It is necessary to measure the stress-strain relationship accurately a-

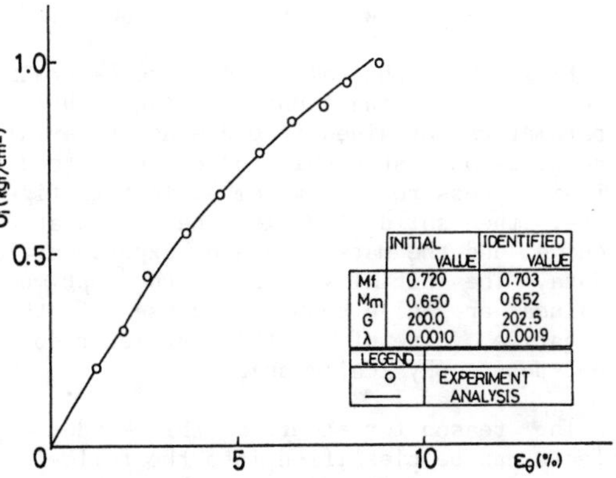

Fig.5 Pressuremeter test result and Identified stress-strain relationship using pressuremeter test result.

Table 2
Sensitivity of constiutitve parameters determined by pressuremeter test result

	Mf x 10^2	Mm x 10^{-1}	G x 10^{-3}	λ x 10^{-9}
Eigen value	0.319	0.346	0.563	0.892
Eigen vector	-0.078	0.733	-0.676	0.001
	0.051	-0.674	-0.737	0.000
	0.000	0.000	-0.001	-1.000*
	0.996*	0.092	-0.015	0.000

round the stress ratio of material failure at which large strain is developed. There exists a component with large absolute value (marked by *) and the other components are very small for the parameters Mf and λ. On the other hand, in the parameter G and Mm more than two components of each eigen vector have large absolute values. This shows that there is an interaction between G and Mm.

6 IDENTIFICATION OF CONSTITUTIVE PARAMETERS USING TRIAXIAL COMPRESSION TEST RESULTS

A stress-strain relation obtained through drained triaxial compression test with constant confining pressure is used to identify the constitutive parameters of Nishi model. For testing, a sand specimen was prepared in a frozen state to get the same relative density as the sand used for pressuremeter test in the soil chamber.

Fig.6 shows the calculated stress-strain relationship using identified constitutive parameters obtained from drained triaxial compression test result for constant confining pressure ($0.5kgf/cm^2$). In this figure, the solid line is the calculated curve and the marks (o) are experimental data. The initial values and the optimum values are also shown. Because of the negative value of λ, this parameter does not posses physical meaning.

The reason for occurring this kind defects can be classified into the following three cases. The first is the case with the reliable constitutive equation but with the unreliable experimental data. This can be overcome by increasing the accuracy of experimental data. The second is the case with reliable experimental data and with the rather simple constitutive equation. The third case is that neither of the two are reliable. Both of second and third cases are commonly occurred. If the number of soil parameters are increased to improve applicability of constitutive equation, some of identified parameters may not have any physical meanings, especially, for the identified parameters which have comparatively small eigen value because a small change in observed data leads to a large change in the estimated parameters. Such parameters should be determined by using data obtained from different test conditions.

Table 3 shows the eigen values and the eigen vectors of constitutive parameters which were identified using drained triaxial compression test result for constant confining pressure ($0.5kgf/cm^2$). Looking at the eigen value of each parameter in this table, it concludes that λ is very sensitive to the error of strain increment because the eigen value of the parameter has the lowest value.

In each eigen vector there exists a component with large absolute value (marked by *) and other components are very small. This implies that the selected constitutive parameters are very reasonable to express soil behavior because these four parameters Mf, Mm, G and compose an orthogonal space by themselves and there is no interaction among them.

There was the interaction between Mm and G in the sensitivity analysis using pressuremeter test result. On the other hand, there is no interaction among them for the case of using drained triaxial compression test results. We discuss this point below.

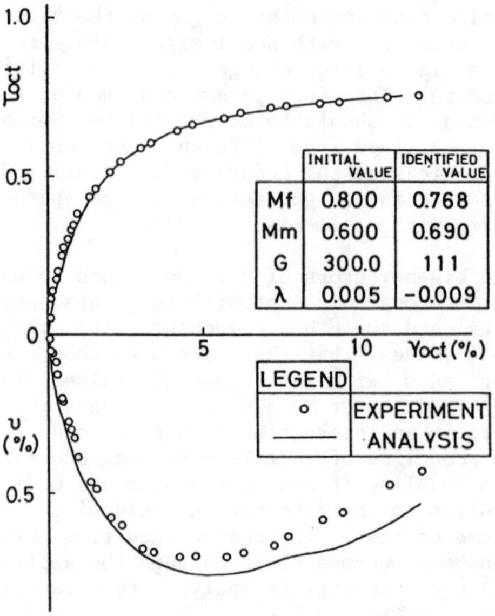

Fig.6 Drained triaxial compression test result and Identified stress-strain relationship.

Table 3
Sensitivity of constitutive parameters determined by draind triaxial compression test result. (Both of $v-\gamma_{oct}$ and $\tau_{oct}-\gamma_{oct}$ relationship are used as observed data)

	$Mf x10^2$	$Gx10^{-1}$	$Mm x10^{-2}$	$\lambda x10^{-8}$
Eigen value	0.154	0.206	0.431	0.420
Eigen vector	1.000*	0.001	0.000	0.000
	0.001	-0.991*	0.138	0.000
	0.000	0.000	0.000	1.000*
	0.000	0.138	0.991*	0.000

7 DISCUSSION

To identify the constitutive parameters using the drained triaxial compression test result, we used two types of data which are concerned with the plastic shear strain and the plastic volumetric strain. Here we investigate effect of the biased data on the identified parameters. Only the plastic volumetric strain is used to identify the constitutive parameters and to analyze sensitivity of them. The results are shown in Fig.7 and Table 4.

In Fig.7, the solid line is the calculated plastic volumetric strain using constitutive parameters at the final step of iteration. The initial values and the optimum values of the constitutive parameters are also shown. It can be seen from this figure that the experimental result is well simulated. Looking at the eigen value of each parameter in Table 4, it decreases in the order of Mf, G, Mm and λ and this tendency agrees well with that shown in Table 3.

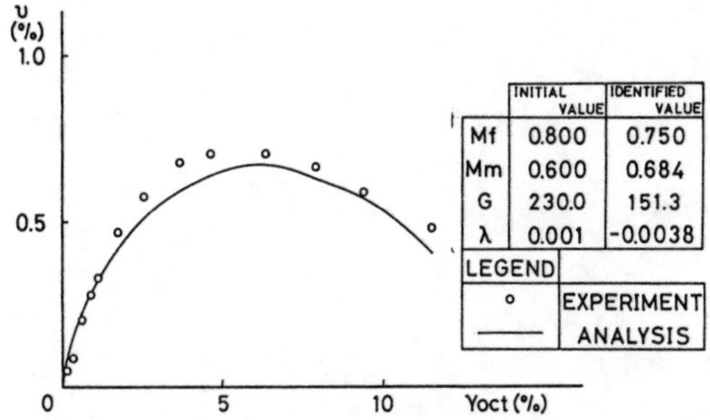

Fig.7 Drained triaxial compression test result and Identified plastic volumetric strain and plastic shear strain relationship.

Table 4
Sensitivity of constitutive parameters determined by drained triaxial compression test results. (only v- relationship ia used as observed data)

Eigen value	$Mf \times 10^{2}$	$Mm \times 10^{-1}$	$G \times 10^{-1}$	$\lambda \times 10^{-10}$
	0.150	0.196	0.214	0.193
Eigen vector	0.397	-0.791	0.467	0.000
	0.904*	-0.248	0.348	0.000
	0.000	0.000	0.000	1.000*
	0.159	0.560	0.813	0.000

From eigen vectors given in Table 4, we can see an interaction between Mm and G. This phenomena in sensitivity analysis was observed in the result using pressuremeter test data. The data obtained from pressuremeter test was the displacement at the borehole surface which corresponds to the volumetric change and the internal pressure only. Therefore there was the interaction among parameters due to lack of the information concerning with shear deformation.

8 CONCLUSIONS

We developed an algorithm to identify in-situ constitutive parameters of soil by using pressuremeter test data. Identification was made possible by choosing parameters to obtain a least square fit between observed and calculated stress strain relationships. Powell's method of minimizing a function of several variables without calculation of derivatives was used to construct an efficient algorithm to make certain convergence in a finite number of iterations. The effect of the initial values on convergence was studied by evaluating the square error between a given response of a pressuremeter in the model ground and the one calculated form the identified parameters. The finite element method was used in our response analysis of the pressuremeter. The main results obtained in this study are

1)The constitutive parameters of sand were identified using pressuremeter test data. The simulated deformation of the probe using identified parameters agreed well the experimental data. Calculating the eigen value and eigen vector of resolution matrix obtained from observed data, the sensitivity of identified parameter to accuracy of observed strain increment was also analyzed.

2)We investigated the effect of element collocation on the simulated deformation field around the pressuremeter. The pressuremeter test was done in the soil chamber to get data to use for identifying constitutive parameters of sand.

3)Comparing the identified parameters using pressuremeter test result with those using triaxial compression test result, it is concluded that the coupling occurred among parameters is caused by the lack of information about shear deformation.

APPENDIX

Identification by Powell's method is fairly sensitive to the initial values of the parameters to be determined, there being possibility to converge to values of para-

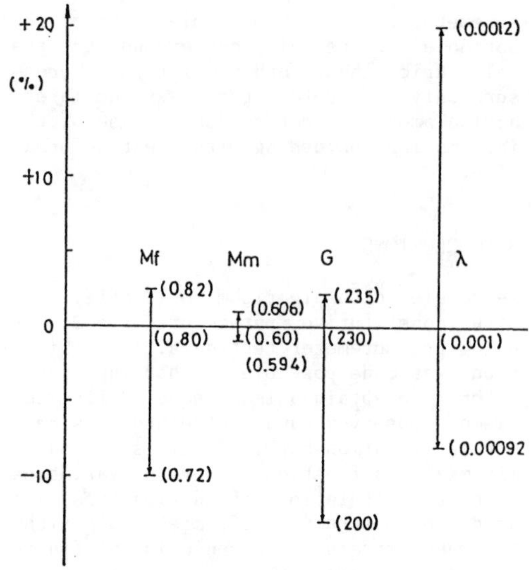

Fig.8 Ranges of initial values which guarantee the convergence of identifying parameters

meters that differ from the real ones. The simulated stress-strain relationship used for the sensitivity analysis given in Table 1 was chosen to test the identifying process. The identifying parameters of the constitutive equation are Mf, Mm, G and λ. Results are given in Fig.8. The ordinate shows the range of initial value with which the convergence to the exact value was achieved. Each range is normalized by the exact value and shown in percent. Although convergence is guaranteed even against the relatively rough initial estimates of λ, the initial value of the parameter that control dilatancy phenomena (Mm) must be carefully selected. The initial values of parameters expressing the condition of material failure (Mf) and the hardening effect (G) must be chosen lower than the exact values.

REFERENCES

[1] Astrom,K.I. & P.Eykhoff 1971. System identification-A survey. Automatica, 7-2, p.123-145.
[2] Sato,T., T.Shibata & T.B.S.Pradhan 1985. Identification of constitutive parameters of soil. Report of ICSMFE, Subcommittee on Constitutive Relation of Soil and Proceedings of Discussion, XIth I.C.S.M.F.E., p.164-167.
[3] Powell,M.J.D. 1967. An efficient method for finding the minimum of a function of several variables without calculating derivatives. Computer Journal, 7, p.155-162.
[4] Zangwill,W.I. 1967. Minimizing a function without calculating derivatives. Computer Journal, 10, p.293-294.
[5] Aki,K. & P.G.Richards 1980. Quantitative seismology-Theory and method. W.H.Freeman and Company, p.675-717.
[6] Nishi,K. & Y.Esashi 1978. Stress strain relationship of sand based on elasto-plasticity theory, Proc. of Japan Society of Civil Engineering, No.280, p.111-122.

Numerical Methods in Geomechanics (Innsbruck 1988), Swoboda (ed.)
© 1989 Balkema, Rotterdam. ISBN 90 6191 809 X

The use of the method of weighted residuals on numerical methods in geomechanics

Yan-Xiang Wang
Shandong Architectural and Structural Engineering Institute, Jinan, People's Republic of China

ABSTRACT: In this paper, the use of the method of weighted residuals (MWR) on numerical method in geomechanics are presented through the well know problems of the consolidation and the slope stability. Besides, taking soil and structure interaction into account, the internal force of the beam on elastic foundation is calculated by using MWR and relatively good results are obtained.

1 INTRODUCTION

The method of weighted residuals (MWR) is mathematical method [1] [2] which directly seeks approximate solutions of the governing differential equations together with their boundary and initial conditions of the applied sciences. It is one of the fairly active methods used in solid mechanics in China.

Due to the needs of seeking for a new numerical method, the MWR has also been studied in the field of geomechanics.

Consider the governing differential equation for u(c, x):

$$F(u) - f = 0 \quad u \text{ in } v$$
$$G(u) - g = 0 \quad u \text{ on } s \qquad (1)$$

where F and G denotes a defferential operator involving derivative of u, v is a three (or two)-dimensional domain and s represents boundary.

Assume a trial function of form:

$$u^* = u(c, x) \qquad (2)$$

where u* are prescribed as the approximating function. Substituting Eq(2) into Eq(1), we have

$$R_I = F(u^*) - f \neq 0$$
$$\text{or} \quad R_b = G(u^*) - g \neq 0 \qquad (3)$$

where R_I and R_b represents domain residuals and boundary residuals respectively.

The obliteration of these residuals can be reached by using equations:

$$\int_v R_I W_I dv = 0$$

$$\int_s R_b W_b dv = 0 \qquad (4)$$

where W is a prescribed weighted function. It yields a set of algebraic equations such that c may be solved and approximate solution of u is obtained.

The program of MWR is simple, and is very suitable for microcomputers. The computer time and the amount of memory space needed for running a programe of MWR are less than that with other methods.

2 APPLICATION OF MWR

2.1 Terzaghi's theory of one-demensional consolidation

The governing differential equation and the boundary and initial conditions are listed below:

$$\frac{\partial u}{\partial t} = c_v \frac{\partial^2 u}{\partial z^2} \qquad \text{(in v)} \qquad (5\text{-a})$$

$$u\Big|_{\substack{t=0 \\ 0\leq z\leq H}} = u_o \qquad \text{(in v)} \qquad (5\text{-b})$$

$$u\Big|_{\substack{t>0 \\ z=0}} = 0 \qquad \text{(on s)} \qquad (5\text{-c})$$

$$\frac{\partial u}{\partial z}\Big|_{\substack{z=H \\ t\geq 0}} = 0 \qquad \text{(on s)} \qquad (5\text{-d})$$

$$u\Big|_{\substack{t\to\infty \\ 0\leq z\leq H}} = 0 \qquad (5\text{-e})$$

where u = pore water pressure,

c_v = coefficient of consolidation.

Assume a trial function of the form

$$u^* = \sum_{m=1}^{\infty} c_m \sin\beta z \cdot e^{-c_v m^2 \beta^2 t} \qquad (6)$$

The trial function satisfies governing differential equation and Eq(5-c) and (5-e). When substituted in Eqs(5-b) and (5-d) we obtain residuals

$$R_{b1} = \sum_{m=1}^{\infty} c_m \sin\beta z\, e^{-c_v m^2 \beta^2 t} - u_o \qquad (7\text{-a})$$

$$R_{b2} = \sum_{m=1}^{\infty} c_m \cos\beta z\, e^{-c_v m^2 \beta^2 t} \qquad (7\text{-b})$$

To obliterating residuals, we have $R_{b2}=0$, and obtain

$$\beta H = \frac{m\pi}{2} \quad (m=1,\ 3,\ 5, \ldots\ldots)$$

$$\beta = \frac{m\pi}{2H} \qquad (8)$$

and let weighted function $W = \frac{\partial R_{b1}}{\partial c_m}$, the obliteration of residuals can be reached by using the method of least square, we have

$$\int_v R_{b2} W dv$$

$$= \int_0^H \left(\sum_{m=1}^{\infty} c_m \sin^2 \frac{m\pi}{2H} z \cdot u_o \sin \frac{m\pi}{2H} z\right) dz$$

$$= \frac{C_m H}{2} - \frac{u_o 2H}{m\pi} = 0$$

hence

$$c_m = \frac{1}{m} \sum \frac{4u_o}{\pi} \qquad (9)$$

therefor

$$u^* = \frac{4u_o}{\pi} \sum_{m=1}^{\infty} \sin \frac{m\pi}{2H} z\, e^{-c_v m^2 \frac{\pi^2}{4H^2} t} \qquad (10)$$

This is an exact solution.

2.2 Consolidation by radial drainage

The problem of one-dimensional radial consolidation is solved by writing the consolidation equation in cylindrical coordinates. It takes form

$$c_r \left(\frac{\partial^2 u}{\partial r^2} + \frac{1}{r}\frac{\partial u}{\partial r}\right) = \frac{\partial u}{\partial t} \qquad (11)$$

Using the method of separation of variables we now rewrite the above equations as follows

$$u(t)\left(\frac{\partial^2 u}{\partial r^2} + \frac{1}{r}\frac{\partial u}{\partial r}\right)$$

$$= \frac{1}{c_r}\frac{\partial u}{\partial t} u\ (r) = \lambda \qquad (12)$$

let $\lambda = -\beta^2$

then, the governing differential equation of the radial drainage consolidation and the boundary and initial conditions are given as follows:

$$r^2 \frac{\partial u^2(r)}{\partial r^2} + r\frac{\partial u(r)}{\partial r} + \beta^2 r^2 u(r) = 0 \quad (\text{ in } v\ ) \qquad (13\text{-a})$$

$$\frac{\partial u(t)}{\partial t} + c_r \beta^2 u\ (t) = 0 \quad (\text{ in } v\ ) \qquad (13\text{-b})$$

$$u \Big|_{\substack{t=0 \\ r_w \le r \le r_e}} = u_o \quad (\text{in } v\ ) \qquad (13\text{-c})$$

$$\frac{\partial u}{\partial r}\Big|_{\substack{t>0 \\ r=r_e}} = 0 \quad (\text{on } s) \qquad (13\text{-d})$$

$$u \Big|_{\substack{t>0 \\ r=r_w}} = 0 \quad (\text{on } s\ ) \qquad (13\text{-e})$$

$$u(t) \Big|_{t=0} = u_o \qquad (13\text{-f})$$

the symbols in Eqs are shown in Fig.1

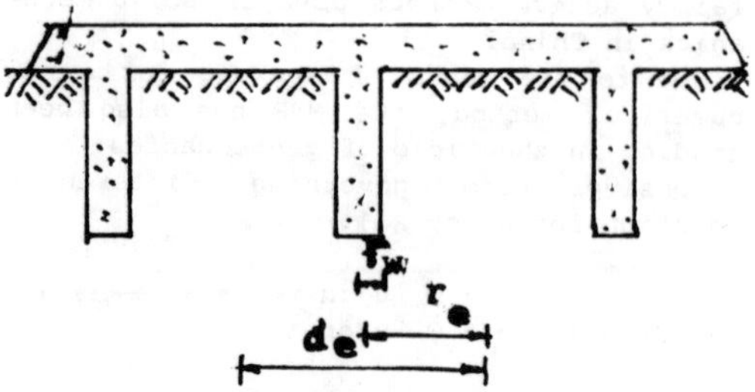

Fig. 1

After above treatment, we have changed partial differential equation to ordinary differential equation. It is apparent that Eq (13-a) is a zero-order Bessel equation.

Assune a trial function has the form

$$u(r) = B\left[r_e^2 \operatorname{Ln}\frac{r}{r_w} - \frac{r^2 - r_w^2}{2}\right] \qquad (14\text{-a})$$

$$u(t) = C\, e^{-c_r \beta^2 t} \qquad (14\text{-b})$$

$$u(r,t) = A\left[r_e^2 \operatorname{Ln}\frac{r}{r_w} - \frac{r^2 - r_w^2}{2}\right] e^{-c_r \beta^2 t} \qquad (14\text{-c})$$

where A = waiting coefficient,
$A = B \cdot C$.
The above function satisfy Eq (13-b) and Eq (13-e), when substituted in Eq (13), we obtain residuals:

$$R_I = -2B + \beta^2 u(r) \qquad (15\text{-a})$$

$$R_{b1} = A\left[r_e^2 \operatorname{Ln}\frac{r}{r_w} - \frac{r^2 - r_w^2}{2}\right] - u_o \qquad (15\text{-b})$$

$$R_{b2} = C e^{o} - u_o \qquad (15\text{-c})$$

To obliterating residuals by the method of moment, we let weighting function $W = r^1$ and obtain from Eq (15-b)

$$\int_{r_w}^{r_e} R_{b1} W dr$$

$$= \int_{r_w}^{r_e} \left\{ A\left[r_e^2 \operatorname{Ln}\frac{r}{r_w} - \frac{r^2 - r_w^2}{2}\right] - u_o \right\} r dr = 0$$

Let $n = \frac{r_e}{r_w}$, we have

$$\frac{A r_e^4}{2}\left[\operatorname{Ln}(n) - \frac{(3n^2-1)(n^2-1)}{4n^4}\right] - \frac{u_o r_e^2}{2}\left[\frac{n^2-1}{n^2}\right] = 0$$

hence

$$A = \frac{4u_o}{d_e^2\left[\frac{n^2}{n^2-1}\operatorname{Ln}(n) - \frac{3n^2-1}{4n^2}\right]} = \frac{4u_o}{d_e^2 F(n)}$$

where $F(n) = \frac{n^2}{n^2-1}\operatorname{Ln}(n) - \frac{3n^2-1}{4n^2}$

Let $R_{b2} = 0$ we get $C = u_o$,
therefor

$$B = \frac{A}{C} = \frac{4}{d_e^2 F(n)}$$

Let $R_I = 0$, from Eq (15-a) we obtain

$$\int_v R_I W \, dv$$

$$= \int_{r_w}^{r_e} \left\{-2B + \beta^2 B\left[r_e^2 \operatorname{Ln}\frac{r}{r_w} - \frac{r^2 - r_w^2}{2}\right]\right\} r dr = 0$$

hence

$$\beta^2 = \frac{2 \times 4}{d_e^2 F(n)} = 2B = \frac{8}{d_e^2 F(n)} \qquad (18)$$

Let $T_r = \frac{c_r t}{d_e^2}$,
therefor

$$u(r,t) = \frac{4u_o}{d_e^2 F(n)}\left[r_e^2 \operatorname{Ln}\frac{r}{r_w} - \frac{r^2 - r_w^2}{2}\right] e^{-\frac{8}{F(n)}T_r} \qquad (19)$$

The solution is the same as that of Barron's [3].

2.3 Slope stability

In fig.2, we can express the factor of safety F_s in the following functional manner

$$F_s = \frac{\sum_{i=1}^{n} F_i(x_i, y_i, y_i')\,dx}{\sum_{i=1}^{n} G_i(x_i, y_i, y_i')\,dx} \qquad (20)$$

$$(\,i = 1,\ 2,\ 3\,)$$

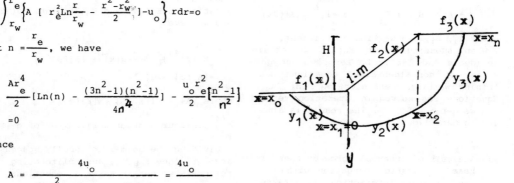

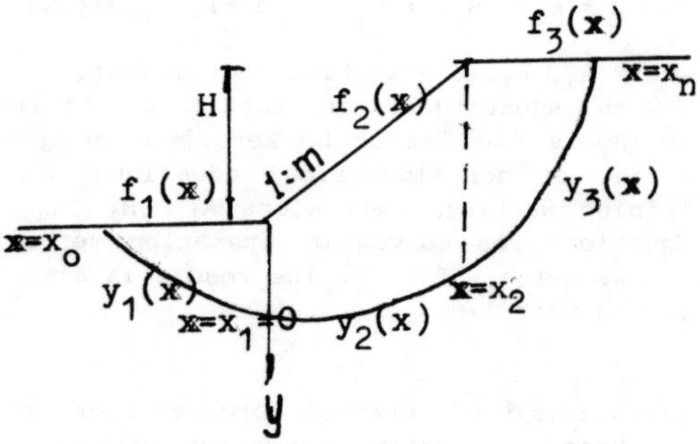

Fig. 2

In the above equation, Euler's equation and transversality equation are [4]:

$$y'' = \frac{\gamma F_s[-A^2 y_i'^3 + A(2A^2-1)y_i'^2 + APy_i' + Q]}{(2CA^2 - 2\gamma A^3 F f_i - 2\gamma A F f_i + 2C) + (2\gamma A^3 F + 2\gamma A F) y_i}$$

$$(\,i = 1,\ 2,\ 3)$$

$$\left.\frac{\partial F_i}{\partial y_i'} - F_s\frac{\partial G_i}{\partial y_i'}\right|_{x=x_i} = \left.\frac{\partial F_{i+1}}{\partial y_{i+1}'} - F_s\frac{\partial G_{i+1}}{\partial y_{i+1}'}\right|_{x=x_i}$$

$$\left.(F_1 - F_s G_1) + (f_1' - y_1')\left(\frac{\partial F_1}{\partial y_1'} - F_s\frac{\partial G_1}{\partial y_1'}\right)\right|_{x=x_o} = 0$$

$$\left.(F_n - F_s G_n) + (f_n' - y_n')\left(\frac{\partial F_n}{\partial y_n'} - F_s\frac{\partial G_n}{\partial y_n'}\right)\right|_{x=x_n} = 0$$

$$(F_j - F_s G_j) + (f'_j - y'_j)\left(\frac{\partial F_j}{\partial y'_j} - F_s \frac{\partial G_j}{\partial y'_j}\right)\Bigg|_{x=x_j}$$

$$= (F_{j+1} - F_s G_{j+1}) + (f'_{j+1} - y'_{j+1})\left(\frac{\partial F_{j+1}}{\partial y'_{j+1}} - F_s \frac{\partial G_{j+1}}{\partial y'_{j+1}}\right)\Bigg|_{x=x_j} \qquad (21)$$

where $A = \frac{tg\phi}{F_s}$

$P = 3A - A^2 f'_i - f'_i$

$Q = A - A^2 f'_i - f'_i$

We use polynomial of degree 2 as a trial function

$$y_i = A_i x^2 + B_i x + C_i \qquad (i = 1, 2, 3) \quad (22)$$

where A_i, B_i, C_i= waiting coefficient.

When substituted in Eq(21) we obtain residuals and let it be zero, we can get a set of non-algebraical equations containing waiting coefficient A_i, B_i, C_i. Equations was solved by iteration method and we get A_i, B_i, C_i. The result is similar to Castillo's [4].

2.4 Analysis of internal force of the beam on elastic foundation with soil and structure interaction being taken into account

The upper structure is simplified to an equivalent beam connected to the beam on elastic foundation.The bending rigidity of the upper structure is calculated by using the formula in [5] and then superimposed that of the beam on foundation as the calculated bending rigidity of the beam of foundation. In this way, the contribution of the upper structure to the foundation is taken into account.

The governing differential equation and boundary condition are

$$EI\frac{d^4w}{dx^4} - q(x) + p(x) = 0$$

$$-EI\frac{d^2w}{dx^2} = -EI\frac{d^3w}{dx^2}\Bigg|_{\substack{x=0\\x=L}} = 0 \qquad (23)$$

where EI = bending rigidity.
Assume a trial function of form

$$w = \sum_{i=0}^{n} a_i \phi_i(x) = [\phi]\{a\} \qquad (24)$$

where $[\phi] = [\ \phi_o\ \phi_1\ \phi_2 \cdots\cdots \phi_n\ ]$

$\{a\} = [\ a_o\ a_1\ a_2 \cdots\cdots a_n\ ]^T$

$\phi = \phi_i(x)$ are a set of the basis function for the Dirac δ-spline function of degree 3,

$\{a\}$ = waiting coefficient.

Subgrade reaction are

$$\{p\} = [K]\{w\} \qquad (25)$$

Substituting Eq(24) into Eq(25) we have

$$\{p\} = [K][\phi]\{a\} \qquad (26)$$

where [K] = the stiffness matrix of foundation. It is calculated by author's method in [6].

Substituted Eq(24) and Eq(26) into Eq(23) and we have

$$R = EI[\phi^{(4)}]\{a\} - q(x) + [K][\phi]\{a\}$$

$$= [A]\{a\} - q(x) \qquad (27)$$

where $[A] = EI[\phi^{(4)}] + [K][\phi]$

$\phi^{(4)}$ is fourth-order derivatives of $\phi_i(x)$ to x.

Dividing the beam into equally-spaced segment, (see Fig. 3) and obliterating the residuals we obtain a set of equations

$$R(x_o) = [A]\{a\} - q(x_o)$$

$$R(x_1) = [A]\{a\} - q(x_1) \qquad (28)$$

$$\cdots\cdots\cdots\cdots\cdots\cdots\cdots$$

$$R(x_n) = [A]\{a\} - q(x_n)$$

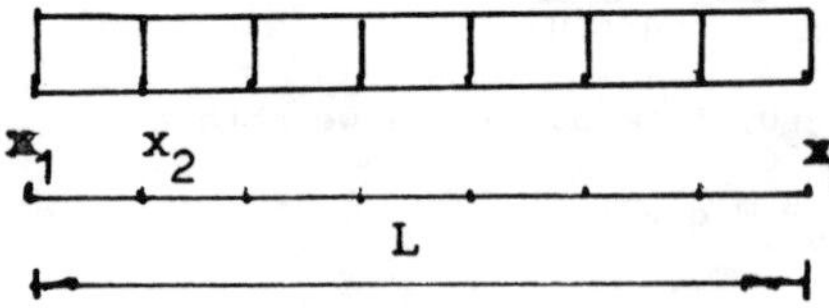

Fig. 3

Eq(28) can be rewritten as follows.

$$[A]\{a\} = \{q\} \qquad (29)$$

We may find out the coefficient $\{a\}$ from Eq(29) and derive $\{w\}$ according to Eq (24). Substituting $\{w\}$ into Eq(25) we obtain subgrade reaction $\{p\}$. Then analyse the force of the beam on foundation by routine method.

3.CONCLUSION

The MWR has many adventages, such as its simplicity, accuracy, short programming, much less computational work, economy and its independence of variational principles with obtainable residuals etc. I believe that the MWR will develop rapidly in geomechanics.

REFERENCES

(1) B. A. Finlayson and L. E. Scriven The method of weighted residuals -A review Applied mechanics reviews, Vol. 19, No 9 (1966).

(2) Xu Cida, Solid mechanics and method of weighted residuals, Tong-Ji University Press, Shanghai, (1987).

(3) Barron, R. A., Consolidation of fine-grained soils by drain wells, Trans. ASCE Vol. 113. (1984).

(4) E. Castillo and J. Revilla, The calculus of variation and the stability of slope, Proc. of the ninth Int. Conf. on soil mechanics and foundation engineering, Vol. 2, session 3. P25, Tokyo, (1977).

(5) Regulation JG60-80 for the Design and Construction of Box Foundation for Tall Buidings, Beijing, (1980).

(6) Wang Yan-Xiang, Finite Element Method of Internal force Analysis of Box Foundation for Tall Buildings on Linear-Elastic and Non-Linear Elastic Soils, Proc. of the Third Int. Conf. on Tall Buildings, Hong Kong and Guangzhou, (1984).

Numerical Methods in Geomechanics (Innsbruck 1988), Swoboda (ed.)
© 1989 Balkema, Rotterdam. ISBN 90 6191 809 X

Some new techniques used in the finite element method programs

Yuan-xun Fan & Man-jing Liu
Water Resources and Hydro-Power Planning and Design Institute MWREP, Beijing, People's Republic of China

ABSTRACT: In developing our finite element method program,we have presented several new techniques to improve its efficiency.They are the automatic generatiothof meshes,the formation of shape functions by a unified formula,the numerical integrations in curved elements and rhe method to calculate the stresses on the element boundaries. They are adopted in our program and proved to be successful.

1. Automatic Generation of Meshes

It is very laborious to make a three dimensional meshes of a solid structure in FEM.Especially for a complicated structure,such as an arch dam etc.,it will take a very long time to finish the meshes of them.If we give some rules to describe the structure, the mesh generation work will be much easier.We can imagine that there will be a longitudinal axis in a structure,along which there are many profiles intersecting the axis at some angle,so the structure consists of many profiles,each profile consists of many edges and each edge consists of many nodes,just like a tree-structure in the graph theory.By properly arranging the node number of the structure in each edge of each profile,we can obtain a topological model of it. With this model we can write a program available to generate the meshes for a group of structures of similar geometric properties. Using this program and a very few input data we can obtain the meshes of a dam,including the node-coordinates,element incidences, material properties,boundary conditions etc..We have analysed an arch dam in Jiangxi province in south of China.The results are good,and the prepareetion work is easy.The essential thought of this method is to controll the topological connections of the model by imposing some restrictions on the numbers of nodes, edges and profiles on each edge, each profile and the entire structure respectively.According to the imposed restrictions,the program will generate the meshes for the corresponding structure. Adopting some elimination algorithm,we can develope this method to solve more complicated problems.

2. Formation of Shape Functions

The shape functions N_i for a n-node element in two or three dimensional space are a group of functions in term of the local coordinates.Each one,N_i,has (n-1) zeros at (n-1) nodes other than P_i,and one value of 1.0 at the node P_i.To form the shape functions we can draw curves C_1,C_2, ...,C_m passing through some of the (n-1) nodes other than P_i, where C_i may be a straight line passing through two nodes,or a circle,or a surface,both passing through more than two nodes.We respresent C_i by an equation as $f_i=0$,then we define the i-th shape function N_i as following:

$$N_i = A_i\ f_1\ f_2 \ldots f_m \qquad (1)$$

where A_i is a constant to be determined.
The shape functions satisfy the following two criteria:

$$1,\ N_i(P_i)=1,\ N_i(P_j)=0\ i\neq j \quad (2)$$
$$2,\ N_1+N_2+\ldots+N_n=1 \quad (3)$$

where $N_i(P_j)$ is the n-th shape function at the node P_j
From the 1-st criterion, we have

$$N_i(P_i)=A_{1i}\ f_1(P_i)f_2(P_i)\ldots f_m(P_i)=1 \quad (4)$$

we can find A_{1i} from (4).
The second criterion can be proved as following:
Suppose L is the number of nodes in an element, put

$$F=N_1+N_2+\ldots+N_L-1 \quad (5)$$

F is a polynomial in term of local coordinates, the highest order of its terms is not greater than L. But F has L zeros at L nodes. So F must be a constant, namely zero.

$$F=0$$

that is $N_1+N_2+\ldots+N_L-1=0$
$N_1+N_2+\ldots+N_L=1$

Q.E.D.

By this method, we can form many useful shape functions, including the serendipity family shape functions. With proper parameters, we can form a formula which is valid for both the corner nodes and the middle edge nodes. e.g. N_i for the 8-node rectangular element

$$N_i(x,y)=|x_i y_i|(1+x_0)(1+y_0)(x_0+y_0-1)/4+(1+x_0+y_0)(1-x^2|y_i|-y^2|x_i|)(1-|x_i y_i|)/2$$
$$i=1,2,\ldots 8 \quad (6)$$

where (x_i, y_i) is the local coordinates of node P_i, and N_i is the i-th shape function.

3. Numerical Integrations in Curved Elements

In the prismatic element or the tetrahedron element, we must calculate the integration as following:

$$I_1=\int_{-1}^{1}\int_{0}^{1-L_1} f(L_1,L_2,L_3)dL_1 dL_2 \quad (7)$$

and

$$I_2=\int_{-1}^{1}\int_{0}^{1-L_1-L_2}\int_{0}^{1-L_1} f(L_1,L_2,L_3,L_4)dL_1 dL_2 dL_3 \quad (8)$$

So we must use methods presented by Radau, Hammer et al, to calculate the integrations. We make some transformations, all the integrations are changed to the following forms:

$$I=\int_{-1}^{1}\int_{-1}^{1}\int_{-1}^{1} g(L_1,L_2,L_3)dL_1 dL_2 dL_3 \quad (9)$$

Now it can be calculated by Gaussian method and is very convenient for calculation.

4. Calculating the Stresses on the Element Boundaries

Fan and Wang have presented an extrapolation matrix to extrapolate the stress from the gauss points to the nodes. It is convenient for the engineers to estimate the stress state in the structures. But it is not very consistent with the boundary conditions. Some small values of stress components often occur on the free load surfaces, according to the extrapolation method. So we suggest an improved method. The nodal stress is calculated by the following formular:

$$\{p\}=[\bar{N}_{ij}]^{-1}\{F\}$$
$$\bar{N}_{ij}=\iint N_i N_j\, ds$$
$$\{F\}=\{k_e\}\{u_e\}-\iiint b\{N\}^T dV$$

where N_i is the i-th shape function.
$\{F\}$ is the element nodal forces
$\{K_e\}$ is the element stiffness matrix
$\{u_e\}$ is the element node displacement
b is the body force
dV volume element
vector $\bar{p}_i=ip_{ix}+jp_{iy}+kp_{iz}$
Projecting $\bar{p}_i$ on the normal to the element boundary surface, we get the normal stress σ at node i
The shear stress τ_i is

$$\tau_i=\sqrt{p_{ix}^2+p_{iy}^2+p_{iz}^2-\sigma^2}$$

On the free surface, there will be no node-force, so $\{p\}$ and σ, τ all of them will be zero, that is accurately consistent with the boundary condition of a free surface.After some proper procedures we can get the stress intensity factor of a crack by this method.

Conclusion

Some techniques are presented in this paper.It is useful to improve the accuracy of the stress results.It is also can calculate the stress concentration factor of a very complicated crack in two or three dimensional space. We hope it will serve for the structure analysis more efficiently in future.

References

Zienkiewicz, O.C.,1977.
The finite element method,3rd.
Mc Graw-Hill.
Hinton,E,Scott,F.C.& E.Rickeetes
1975.Local least squares stress smothing parabolic isoparametric elements,Int. J.Num.Meth.Engng. 1979,9:235-238.
Fan Y.X & Wang S.J. 1979.
On the application of an interpolation matrix for computation of stresses in finite elements. Proc.Third Int. Conf.on Num.Meth. in Geomechanics.1273-1280.
Fan Y.X. & Jiang Y.L.1983.
Numerical Integrations for Curved Isoparametric Elements. Report at Conference on Civil Engineering Conputer Applivations,Lushan
(In Chinese)

Numerical Methods in Geomechanics (Innsbruck 1988), Swoboda (ed.)
© 1989 Balkema, Rotterdam. ISBN 90 6191 809 X

Constitutive equations and the effect of the axiom of incompressibility on the creep of rock salt

F.T.Suorineni
University of Science and Technology, School of Mines, Tarkwa, Ghana

Abstract

An investigation into the effect of the axiom of incompressibility on the creep behaviour of rock salt is conducted. Fundamental constitutive equations for the two stress states of loading (uniaxial and triaxial) are given. The results show that confining pressure has an influence on the creep behaviour of rock salt up to a critical value of 25 MPa. A boundary deviatoric stress of 12 MPa has also been established, beyond which strain-hardening effect due to creep in uniaxial loading is significant. This effect is absent or little for triaxial loading due to the change of state of the material from brittle to ductile under confinement. The creep constants m and n in the time-hardening law, are found to be the most important parameters in the establishment of the critical limits and in discussing the brittle – ductile transition of the material. The results are found to be of relevance in the design of mine pillars and the control of peripheral rocks in tunnels in rock salt. They are also important for cutting down costs of laboratory creep tests.

1 Introduction

It is well known that materials with identical chemical composition and geometric shapes often differ in the manner in which they respond to equal excitations or forces. This difference in response to impact is attributed to the difference in internal constitution of the materials. Equations characterizing the individual material and its reaction to external excitations are called "Constitutive Equations". This implies that the adequate representations of material properties by constitutive equations will require the handling of several variables leading to complex mathematical solutions. In practice, these variables are often so chosen or certain basic assumptions made, that the resultant equations are simple and yet without any loss of accuracy.

In this paper tensors are used to develop constitutive equations related to the axiom of incompressibility on the mechanical behaviour of rock salt. Today, much work is being done on the creep of rocks and other materials in various fields, under complex stress systems. One reason for this is to simulate in-situ conditions. In analysing the results of these tests, investigators have generally made the drastic assumption that if a hydrostatic stress be added to the components of a complex stress system, then the only effect of this stress on the corresponding strain system would be to give rise to additional volumetric strain, leaving creep strains and rates unaffected. This means that given stress states which differ only by a state of hydrostatic stress may be expected to produce identical deformation.

2 Implications of the incompressibility assumptions

In general, the stress tensor is denoted by σ_{ij}. Subscripts i and j take values from 1 to 3. The stress tensor can be split into two components, namely

1 the deviatioric stress and
2 the hydrostatic stress

for a case of principal stresses only as in the laboratory creep tests

$$\sigma_{ij} = \begin{bmatrix} \sigma_1 & \sigma & \sigma \\ \sigma & \sigma_2 & \sigma \\ \sigma & \sigma & \sigma_3 \end{bmatrix} \tag{1}$$

where $\sigma_1 > \sigma_2 > \sigma_3$

$$\sigma_{ij} = s_{ij} + \frac{1}{3}\delta_{ij}\sigma_{kk} \tag{2}$$

where

$$\delta_{ij} = \begin{cases} 1 \; for \; i = j \; Kronecker \\ 0 \; for \; i \neq j \; constant \end{cases}$$

$\frac{1}{3}\delta_{ij}\sigma_{kk}$ = hydrostatic stress component.

From (2)

$$\sigma_{ij} = \begin{bmatrix} s_1 & 0 & 0 \\ 0 & s_2 & 0 \\ 0 & 0 & s_3 \end{bmatrix} + \frac{1}{3}\begin{bmatrix} \sigma_{kk} & 0 & 0 \\ 0 & \sigma_{kk} & 0 \\ 0 & 0 & \sigma_{kk} \end{bmatrix} \quad (3)$$

and from equations (1) and (2),

$$\begin{aligned} \sigma_1 &= s_1 + \tfrac{1}{3}\sigma_{kk} \\ \sigma_2 &= s_2 + \tfrac{1}{3}\sigma_{kk} \\ \sigma_3 &= s_3 + \tfrac{1}{3}\sigma_{kk} \end{aligned} \quad (4)$$

Thus: $s_{ij} = \sigma_{ij} - \frac{1}{3}\delta_{ij}\sigma_{kk}$

Division of the state of stress into a hydrostatic stress component and a deviatoric stress system is important because of the differences in mechanical behaviour of materials under each of these components.

The hydrostatic stress component is assumed to be associated with change in volume. It is also related to the transformation of brittle materials to ductile ones (Farmer [3]). The concept of distortion lessness associated with hydrostatic stress tensor is popular with many investigators, (Baley [1], Prager [9] and Johnson [6]). Deviatoric stress is related to distortion of materials and many materials obey an "energy of distortion criterion" of elastic breakdown (Jaeger [5]). The mechanical effects of the two components are independent, even though they act simultaneously as in the triaxial tests.

From equation (1), for a uniaxial creep test where $\sigma_2 = \sigma_3 = 0$:

$$\sigma_{ij} = \begin{bmatrix} s_1 & 0 & 0 \\ 0 & 0 & 0 \\ 0 & 0 & 0 \end{bmatrix} \quad (5)$$

for triaxial creep tests;

$$\begin{aligned} \sigma_{ij} &= \begin{bmatrix} s_1 & 0 & 0 \\ 0 & 0 & 0 \\ 0 & 0 & 0 \end{bmatrix} + \tfrac{1}{3}\begin{bmatrix} \sigma_{kk} & 0 & 0 \\ 0 & \sigma_{kk} & 0 \\ 0 & 0 & \sigma_{kk} \end{bmatrix} \\ &= \tfrac{1}{3}\begin{bmatrix} 3s_1 + \sigma_{kk} & 0 & 0 \\ 0 & \sigma_{kk} & 0 \\ 0 & 0 & \sigma_{kk} \end{bmatrix} \end{aligned} \quad (6)$$

If the assumption concerning the hydrostatic stress is valid, then the principal creep strains and rates for equations (5) and (6) should be equal. This implies that the creep rates for a given deviatoric stress level at the different states of confining pressures should be equal.

3 Previous work

The effect of hydrostatic pressure on creep is of great importance since it will define a depth in the earth's crust above which it is possible for steady state to occur. Le Compte [7] and Schmidt [10] examined the effect of confining pressure on the creep of artificial rock salt samples and concluded that it has small influence on the time dependent strain. In 1964, Thompson and Repperger made an attempt probably the first, to investigate the effect of confining pressure on the steady state creep rate of halite and sylvinite. They concluded that the hydrostatic pressure does affect the creep rate to some extent but was negligible when compared to axial stresses for the confined and unconfined states.

Christy [2] observed that hydrostatic pressure strongly depresses the steady state creep of sylver bromide. Pfeifle and Senseny [8] determined a constitutive model for the steady state creep of natural rock salt using data obtained from triaxial compression but did not state the contribution of hydrostatic pressure. Williams and Elizzi [13] concluded that confinement has sufficiently far reaching effects on creep of gypsum. They also conducted a limited number of tests on anhydrite at low confining pressures and obtained similar results. Thus as can be observed, the effect of confining pressure on the creep behaviour of rock salt is not a simple one and still requires further investigation.

4 Objective of present study

The main objective of the present study is to investigate the effect of hydrostatic pressure on the creep behaviour of rock salt using the deviatoric and hydrostatic stress states, in particular, the level at which its effect may be considered significant and to throw more light on the questions surrounding the concept.

5 Test procedures

In order to achieve the objectives of the investigation, for a given deviatoric stress level different confining pressures were added at increments of 5 MPa. In all five different deviatoric stress levels were used. To each stress level five different confining pressures were added at various intervals to a given specimen. For each deviatoric stress level two identical tests were conducted for comparison, putting the total number of test specimens at 20. Fifty triaxial tests were thus conducted as against 10 uniaxial tests. Table 1 gives the pressure schedule for the multiple-step-creep and uniaxial creep tests.

Multiple-step-creep tests have the advantance of reducing variation in results due to intrinsic structural differences which are more likely when different samples are used. In the former case all inherent structural features are the same – creep tests are sensitive to environmental conditions. In this study the tests were conducted at an ambient temperature of $23.5^\circ \pm 3.5^\circ C$

with a relative humidity of 43% RH as measured with an independent hygrometer. Recorders were used for the monitoring of these variables.

The creep rigs used were developed by the University of Newcastle Upon Tyne and details are given by Horseman [4]. Details of sample loading are given by Suorineni [11]. For the uniaxial creep tests, a time span between 130 and 170 days was covered while the triaxial multiple-step-creep tests took 180 days in all.

6 Test results and their discussion

6.1 Uniaxial Creep Test

Typical creep strain-time curves are given in Fig.1 for uniaxial compressive stresses of 14.5 MPa. The "hump" shown after 112 days is due to increase in humidity as a result of a break down of the humidifier. The severity of this effect gradually decreases with increasing deviatoric stress from 6 MPa up to 14.5 MPa, where the effect is almost absent. This is because at low deviatoric stress levels the creep strains are significantly enhanced by humidity whilst at high deviatoric stress levels the effect is suppressed. At low deviatoric stress levels the imposed stresses are ineffective in giving an instantaneous rearrangement and compaction of crystal grains in the matrix. The process of grain rearrangement is therefore a gradual one resulting in a slow decrease in strain rate. It is probably this process which is responsible for the "wavy" nature of creep curves and less strain-hardening at low stresses. Indeed, for polycrystalline materials like rock salt the large crystal characteristic of the material will speed up the said process. At high deviatoric stresses the imposition of such stresses on polycrystalline specimens results in instantaneous rearrangement and compaction of crystal grains. It is this rapid rearrangement and compaction which is responsible for the high initial strain rates (elastic strains). The process here is thus short lived and movement is no longer significant by crystal matrix deformation. The consequences of this is strain-hardening at such stress levels.

The corresponding creep rate-time curve for the deviatoric stress level is given in Fig.2.

6.2 Multiple-Step Triaxial Creep Tests

A plot of creep strains verses time shows the development of "plateaus" after 130 days as seen in Fig.3 for a deviatoric stress of 12 MPa but are absent for deviatoric stresses above this level, as shown in Fig.4 for a deviatoric stress of 17.5 MPa.

This special feature is due to the increase in humidity as a result of the humidifeir breakdown discussed earlier. It is observed that after elimination of elastic strains the creep curves usually to not show any "steps" accompanying the change, (increase) in confining pressures. This could be said to mean that the subsequent confining pressures suppress creep rates or result in very little movements.

Comparison of the creep curves for the uniaxial and Multiple-step triaxial tests show that strain-hardening has little effect on triaxial creep tests as compared with the uniaxial tests at equal deviatoric stress levels. This behaviour could be attributed to the change of state of the material – brittle to ductile, on application of confining pressures.

Fig.5 shows the creep strain rate against time curves for deviatoric stress level of 14.5 MPa. They show higher strain rates for the triaxial tests.

The creep constants m, n and A in equation (7) were used to investigate the material behaviour under the varios stress systems in the study.

$$\begin{aligned} \xi &= A\,\sigma^n t^m\,(time) \\ &= B\,t^m \end{aligned} \qquad (7)$$

where $B = A\,\sigma^n$
This equation can be transformed by differentiation into the expression:

$$\dot{\xi} = B_2\,\sigma^n \qquad (8)$$

where $B_2 = mt^{n-1}$

7 Determination of the creep constants

The creep constants were determined using a Least Squares curve fitting programme with the IBM-320 computer of NUMAC. By regressing ϵ (strain) against t (time), m and B were obtained from equation (7). For comparison, strain rate was also regressed against t as in the equation.

$$\dot{\xi} = B_3 t^k \qquad (9)$$

where $k = m - 1$
and $B_3 = mA\sigma^n$

The n values obtained from the two approaches for the uniaxial tests are given in Table 2. It can be observed that these values agree fairly well.

For the multiple-step creep tests it was not possible to regress directly for the various regions associated with the different confining pressure increments.

A preliminary approach of sectional analysis was not very successful. This could be attributed to the small movements following the confining pressure increments. The method was abandoned in favour of a "Continuous Successive Regression Method" (CSRM). By this method creep data obtained for the first confining pressures are regressed to obtain the constants for that section.

The regression range is then extended to include data from the second confining pressure increment and the constants obtained. This process is continued until the whole range of confining pressures is covered. Results obtained by this method are given in Table 3 and Fig.6 is a curve fitting graph to illustrate the method.

The stress exponent n was obtained by regression using the equation

$$\xi = B_1 \sigma^n \tag{10}$$

where $B_1 = At^m$
Alternatively the equation

$$\dot{\xi} = B_4 \sigma^n \tag{11}$$

where $B_4 = mAt^{m-1}$ could have been used.

Results obtained from this method are given in Table 4.

8 Conclusions and recommendations

The constant m is seem to be generally lower for the uniaxial tests than the triaxial tests. It shows no deviator stress dependece but appears to be controlled by hydrostatic pressures. In general, m increases with confining pressure up to about 25 MPa after which it levels out and remains fairly constant as shown in Table 3.

It is observed from this table that for the same deviatoric stress to which 2 different samples were used there are differences in the value of m for the corresponding confining pressures. These Difference may be due to the differences in the intrinsic structural properties. What is remarkable for all the tests is that for each sample the m values are consistent in that they become constant after a confining pressure of 25 MPa. 25 MPa could be said to be the critical confining pressure for rock salt, above which hydrostatic pressure has little or no effect on its behaviour.

The creep constants A, m and n are material constants and depend among other factors such as: temperature and anisotropy. m and n are strain-hardening parameters and they increase as the material changes from brittle to ductile. m appears more sensitive to confining pressure changes than n.

Strain-hardening occours at deviatoric stress levels in the range $(\sigma_1 - \sigma_3) \geq 12\ MPa$ in uniaxial creep tests. It is suppressed at equivalent stress levels in triaxial tests. It is suggested that for triaxial creep tests on rock salt the use of confining pressures above 25 MPa may not be necessary and that the paramenters m and n should be used as a measure of strain-hardening and in the brittle-ductile behaviour analysis of rock salt. Confinement should therefore be taken into consideration up to a depth (about 1.000m), equivalent to 25 Mpa, beyond which it has negligible influence on design of structure such as mine pillars and peripheral rock in tunnels.

References

[1] Bailey, R.W. *1951. Creep relationships and application to pipes, tubes and cylindrical parts under internal pressure.* Proc.I. Mech.E., Vol.164, pp 425 – 431

[2] Christy, R.N. *1956. Creep of sodium chloride and sodium bromide at high temperature.* Acta Metallurgica Vol.2, pp 284

[3] Farmer, I.W. *1980. Face and roadway stability in underground coal mines; geotechnical criteria.* Rpt. to N.C.B. Dept. Mining Eng., University of Newcastle Upon Tyne

[4] Horseman, S.T. *1979. An evaluation of the rheological properties of rock salt for creep storage cavity design* Ph.D. Thesis, University of Newcastle Upon Tyne

[5] Jaeger, L.G. *1980. Cartesian tensors in engineering science.* Pergamon Press

[6] Johnson, A.E. *1950. Creep under complex stress systems at elevated temperatures.* Inst. Mechanical Engineers, London, Vol.164, pp 432 – 447

[7] Le Compte, P. *1965. Creep in rock salt.* Jour. Geol. Vol.73, N3, pp 469 – 484

[8] Pfeifle, T.W. and Senseny, P.E. *1982. Steady state creep of rock salt in geoengineering.* 23rd Symp. Rock Mech., pp 307 – 314

[9] Prager, W. *1945. Strain hardening under combined stresses.* J. Applied Physics, Vol.16, pp 837 – 840

[10] Schmidt, W. *1939. Festigkeit und Verfestigung von Steinsatz.* ZANM - A Vol.1, pp 1 – 29

[11] Suorineni, F.T. *1983. Effect of axiom of incompressibility to the mechanical behaviour of rock salt.* M.Sc. Dissertation, Dept. of Mining Engineering, University of Newcastle Upon Tyne

[12] Thompson, E. and Ripperger, E.A. *1964. An experimental technique for investigation of the flow of halite and sylvinite.* Proc. 6th Symp., Rock Mech., Rolla, Missouri., pp 467 – 487

[13] Williams, F.T. and Elizzi, M.A. *1977. Creep properties of sherburn gypsum.* Conf. Rock Engineering Bri. Geotech. Soci., pp 71 – 83

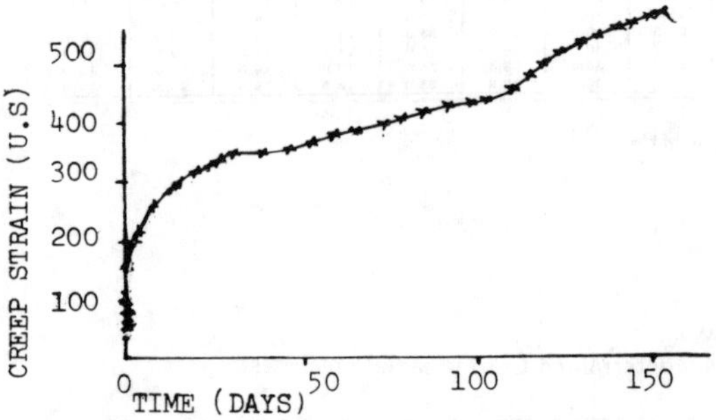

Figure 1: Creep Strain Vs. Time curve for specimen No.2/10U. Uniaxial compresive stress = 14.5 MPa.

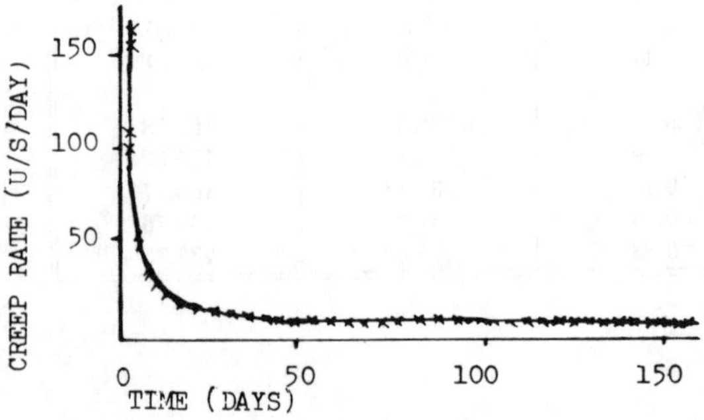

Figure 2: Creep Rate Vs. Time curve for specimen No.2/10U. Uniaxial compresive stress = 14.5 MPa.

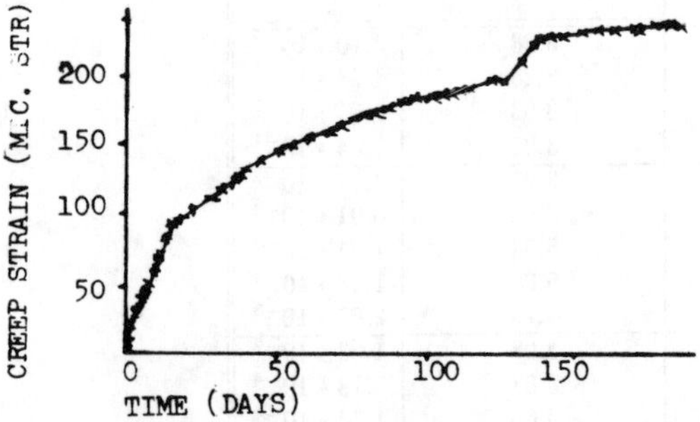

Figure 3: Creep Strain Vrs. Time curve: step-load test (2/5T). Deviatoric stress = 12 MPa. Confining pressures: 15, 20, 25, 30, 35 MPa.

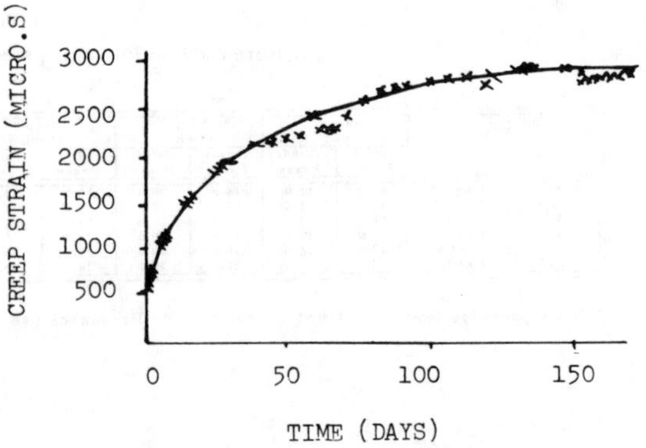

Figure 4: Creep Strain Vs. Time curve: Step-load test (3/4T). Deviatoric stress = 17.5 MPa. Confining pressure: 15, 20, 25, 30, 35 MPa.

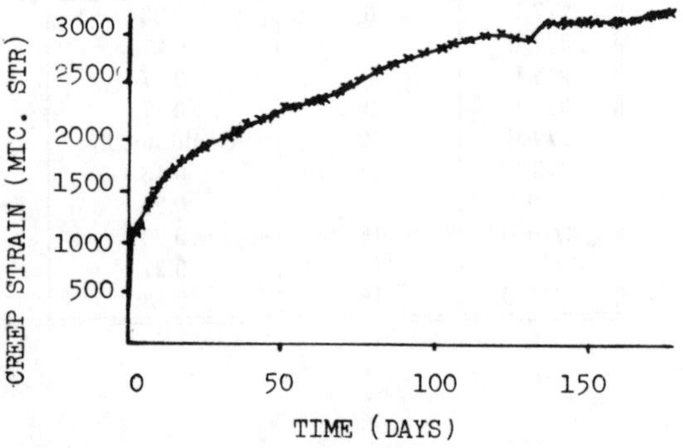

Figure 5: Creep Rate Vs. Time curve: Step-load Test (3/3T). Deviatoric stress = 14.5 MPa. Confining pressure: 15, 20, 25, 30, 35 MPa.

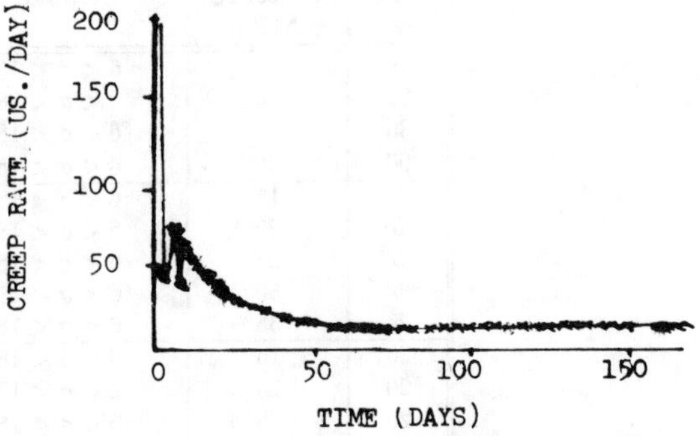

Figure 6: Curve fitting for Time exponent m and contant-A (illustration)

Table 1

Pressure scedule for multiple-step-creep and uniaxial creep tests

$\sigma_1 - \sigma_3$ (MPa)	Rig.No.	Step one		Step two		Step three		Step four		Step five		Accumulator Pressure		Uniaxial Rigs	
		Axial Press	Conf. Press	Axial Press	Conf. Press	Axial Press	Conf. Press	Axial Press	Conf. Press	Axial Press	Conf. Press	Axial Press	Conf. Press	Axial Press	Accum. Press
6	1 and 2	11.0	15.0	14.0	20.0	16.5	25.0	19.0	30.0	22.0	35.0	10.5	14.5	6.0	4.0
9	3 and 4	18.0	15.0	15.5	20.0	18.0	25.0	21.0	30.0	23.5	35.0	10.5	14.5	9.0	6.0
12	5 and 6	14.5	15.0	17.0	20.0	19.5	25.0	22.5	30.0	25.0	35.0	14.0	14.5	12.0	8.0
15	7 and 8	16.0	15.0	18.5	20.0	21.5	25.0	24.0	30.0	26.5	35.0	15.5	14.5	19.5	10.0
18	9 and 10	17.5	15.0	20.5	20.0	23.0	25.0	25.5	30.0	28.5	35.0	17.0	14.5	17.5	12.0
21*	11 and 12	19.0	15.0	22.0	20.0	24.5	25.0	28.0	30.0	30.0	35.0	18.5	14.5	20.5	14.0

* This pressure level could not be recovered. Pressures are all in MPa

Table 2

Creep constants - time exponent M and A - determined from uniaxial creep tests

Specimen No.	Deviatoric Stress MPa	Time exponent m from Strain-time fitting	Time exponent m from Rate-time fitting	Creep constant A from Strain-time fitting	Creep Constant A from Rate-time fitting
2/7 U	6	0.23	0.23	7.41	7.39
3/7 U	6	0.27	0.27	6.10	6.20
2/8 U	9	0.17	0.13	58.39	69.96
3/8 U	9	0.17	0.17	28.70	28.70
2/9 U	12	Could not fit	-	-	-
3/9 U	12	0.13	0.13	106.90	107.58
2/10 U	15	0.21	0.19	164.11	175.50
3/10 U	15	0.20	0.15	137.17	160.77
2/11 U	18	0.21	0.18	247.44	264.76
3/11 U	18	0.18	0.13	223.80	272.75

Table 4

Creep constants determined from uniaxial and triaxial multiple-step creep tests at $23.5 \pm 3.5^{o}C$

Time in	Confining Pressure MPa	Deviatoric Stress Range	Stress Exponent n	Constant A
5	0	$6 < \sigma < 18$	3.28	$3.10 * 10^{-2}$
20	0	$6 < \sigma < 18$	3.25	$4.24 * 10^{-2}$
30	0	$6 < \sigma < 18$	3.03	$7.61 * 10^{-2}$
90	0	$6 < \sigma < 18$	3.01	$1.04 * 10^{-1}$
5	15	$6 < \sigma < 18$	3.25	$4.18 * 10^{-2}$
5	20	$6 < \sigma < 18$	3.58	$6.01 * 10^{-2}$
5	25	$6 < \sigma < 18$	5.54	$1.91 * 10^{-4}$
5	30	$6 < \sigma < 18$	5.88	$1.03 * 10^{-4}$
5	35	$6 < \sigma < 18$	4.78	$2.67 * 10^{-3}$
20	15	$6 < \sigma < 18$	3.98	$1.23 * 10^{-2}$
20	20	$6 < \sigma < 18$	3.83	$3.18 * 10^{-4}$
20	25	$6 < \sigma < 18$	5.60	$1.74 * 10^{-4}$
20	30	$6 < \sigma < 18$	5.45	$4.39 * 10^{-4}$
20	35	$6 < \sigma < 18$	Not up to 20 days	

Table 3
Creep constants – time exponent m and A from triaxial multiple-step creep tests

Specimen No.	Deviatoric Stress $\sigma_1 - \sigma_3$ MPa	Confining Pressure Range Regressed (MPa)	Time Exponent m	Creep Constant A	Elastic Strain (US)
2/1 T	6	15	0.29	27.40	324
		15 - 20	0.31	27.07	488
		15 - 25	0.32	26.90	560
		15 - 30	0.32	26.64	630
		15 - 35	0.33	26.57	728
3/1 T	6	15	0.32	99.82	222
		15 - 20	0.34	95.70	339
		15 - 25	0.36	91.80	421
		15 - 30	0.37	89.23	502
		15 - 35	0.38	88.32	591
2/2 T	9	15	0.29	39.91	371
		15 - 20	0.26	43.25	719
		15 - 25	0.27	43.11	833
		15 - 30	0.27	42.90	947
		15 - 35	0.27	42.80	1001
3/2 T	9	15	0.29	34.06	407
		15 - 20	0.31	49.97	575
		15 - 25	0.45	24.21	663
		15 - 30	0.46	24.00	782
		15 - 35	0.46	24.00	824
2/5 T	12	15	0.39	30.84	1124
		15 - 20	0.41	28.04	1393
		15 - 25	0.41	29.15	1518
		15 - 30	0.48	23.44	1620
		15 - 35	0.49	22.61	1786
3/5 T	12	15	0.52	34.57	2380
		15 - 20	Logarithmic Law		2811
		15 - 25	in all cases		2975
		15 - 30	0.33	69.61	3075
		15 - 35	0.32	70.16	3185
3/3 T	15	15	0.20	200.93	842
		15 - 20	0.26	206.70	1837
		15 - 25	0.25	208.57	2077
		15 - 30	0.25	209.36	2203
		15 - 35	0.25	209.75	2303
2/3 T	15	15	0.29	205.10	894
		15 - 20	0.32	199.56	1274
		15 - 25	0.33	197.71	1545
		15 - 30	0.34	193.53	1706
		15 - 35	0.34	192.90	1824
3/4 T	18	15	0.29	748.18	1422
		15 - 20	0.29	751.18	3091
		15 - 25	0.28	752.38	3330
		15 - 30	0.28	755.01	3514
		15 - 35	0.28	756.57	3661
2/4 T	18	15	0.37	319.16	1214
		15 - 20	0.40	317.47	1456
		15 - 25	0.40	316.17	1687
		15 - 30	0.40	315.51	1863
		15 - 35	0.40	315.54	2003

Numerical Methods in Geomechanics (Innsbruck 1988), Swoboda (ed.)
© 1989 Balkema, Rotterdam. ISBN 90 6191 809 X

The consolidation of soils with very low permeability

C.Cherubini & C.I.Giasi
Istituto di Geologia Applicata e Geotecnica, Facoltà di Ingegneria, Bari, Italy

G.Vacca
Istituto di Macchine ed Energetica, Facoltà di Ingegneria, Bari, Italy

ABSTRACT: A study has been carried out to investigate whether Darcy's law might still be applicable for describing the process of consolidation of fine-grained soils. The development of a one-dimensional numerical model worked out on a computer with a very simple finite difference scheme has made it possible to show how for such soils the dissipation process of the excess pore pressures is slower than the phenomenon predicted by using classic Terzaghi's theory, |1|. Such a "delay" is more accentuated the greater the deviation from Darcy's law and the smaller the amount of initial excess pore pressure.

INTRODUCTION

The solution of a number of hydraulic problems in soils has been based on Darcy's law, in the past. However, for coarse soils (gravel, rock fills) it has been noted for some time that the relation between flow velocity and hydraulic gradient is regulated by non-linear empirical laws, |2|. A further discrepancy with respect to Darcy's law can be noted for soils (such as silts and clays) that have a low or a very low degree of permeability, |3|. In particular figure 1 (from bibl. 3) shows how the deviation from Darcy's law is more and more marked as the coefficient of permeability k is reduced.

For soils with a lower degree of permeability (e.g. overconsolidated clays), the above mentioned authors have identified an initial behavior characterized by a potential law, tangent in a given point of abscissa 'i_e' (transitional gradient), to the straight line, the prolongation of which meets the axis of the abscissa at a point 'i_o', known as the initial gradient.

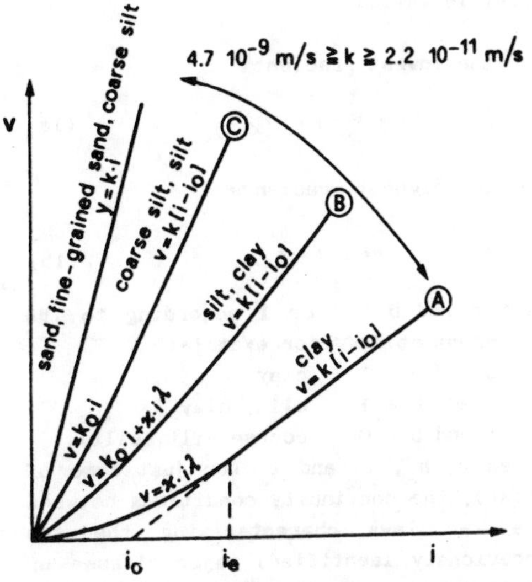

Figure 1. Correlation between types of soil and relevant filtration laws.

Nendza and Gabener themselves |3,4| indicate the most likely values of 'i_o' and 'i_e' as a function of the type of soil affected by the flow.

These studies, which came after those of Hansbo |5| have suggested to the authors the opportunity of modifying Terzaghi's theory of one-dimensional consolidation, with the aim of evaluating the influence of the modified laws v=v(i).

PROPOSED NUMERICAL MODEL

Terzaghi's classic theory of consolidation |1| is based on the following hypotheses:

- the volumetric compressibility coefficient (m_v) is constant for all points of the layer and for each consolidation stage;
- the water flows only along vertical paths;
- the delay in the reduction of the layer thickness is caused exclusively by the low degree of permeability of the soil, which consequently makes the effect of secondary negligible compression.

With those hypotheses and assuming that the proposed law of Nendza and Gabener |3,4| is valid:

for the lowest gradient

$$v = a(k_o i) + b(\varkappa i^{\lambda}) \quad (1a)$$

for the highest gradients

$$v = k(i - i_o) \quad (1b)$$

with a and b = 0 or 1 according to the different soils, (for example:

a = 0 and b = 1 clay
a = 1 and b = 1 silt, clay
a = 1 and b = 0 coarse silt, silt),

given k, h_o, i_o and i_e (or just some of those), the continuity conditions between the two laws characterizing the two (previonsly identified) major classes of soils, produce the following:

- if a = 0 and b = 1

$$\lambda = \frac{i_e}{i_e - i_o} \quad \varkappa = \frac{k(i_e - i_o)}{i_e{}^{\lambda}} = \frac{k}{\lambda \cdot i_e{}^{\lambda}} \quad (2a)$$

- if a = b = 1

$$\lambda = [1 - \frac{k\, i_o}{i_e(k - k_o)}]^{-1} \quad \varkappa = \frac{k - k_o}{\lambda \cdot i_e{}^{\lambda - 1}} \quad (2b)$$

- if a = 1 and b = 0

$$\frac{k_o}{k} = 1 - \frac{i_o}{i_e} \quad (2c)$$

It should also be mentioned that, in this preliminary stage of our investigation, the problem of consolidation is solved for the case of constant excess pore pressure value at the initial time over the whole layer examined.

As will be seen further on, the 'modified' consolidation process is fairly markedly influenced by the value of that initial overpressure; this is not the case, though, if the classic theory is used.

Consider now a thin horizontal layer that is part of a deposit in the process of consolidation. The thickness of the layer be dz, the velocity of the flowing water v and the excess pore pressure (u/ z)dz. As briefly mentioned before, the consolidation phenomenon is governed by the following equations:

$$v = a(-\frac{k_o}{\gamma_w}\frac{\partial u}{\partial z}) + b[(-\frac{1}{\gamma_w}\frac{\partial u}{\partial z})^{\lambda}\varkappa], \text{ if } i \le i_e \quad (3)$$

$$v = k(i - i_o), \qquad \text{if } i > i_e \quad (4)$$

The mass equilibrium, then, leads to the following expression:

$$\frac{\partial v}{\partial z} = -m_v \frac{\partial u}{\partial t} \quad (5)$$

and thus equations (3) and (4), using eqn. (5), become

$$u_t = \{ a[\frac{k_o}{m_v \gamma_w}] + b[\frac{\varkappa \lambda}{m_v \gamma_w{}^{\lambda}}(-u_z)^{\lambda - 1}]\} u_{zz}$$

$$\text{if } i \le i_e \quad (6)$$

$$u_t = \frac{k}{m_v \gamma_w} u_{zz}, \qquad \text{if } i > i_e \quad (7)$$

Obviously, the solutions to these equations depend on the bydraulic boundary conditions, and thus on the pressume and drainage present there. Here, the case of bilateral drainage is considered with constant excess pore pressure at the instant $t = 0$. The hypothesis made on the flow velocity in the range of $i < ie$ has introduced a non-linearity into equation (6) which governs the consolidation phenomenon of the layer, and this non-linearity makes a solution in an analytical form impossible. On the contrary, it is possible to solve the equations numerically with a satisfactory degree of accuracy by means of finite difference schemes. Since we are interested in a transitory phenomenon, a very simple explicit technique |6| has been preferred which makes it possible to reproduce the dynamics of the consolidation process in a straightforward and accurate way.

With this aim in mind, it has been decided to "adimensionalize" the equations, assuming as reference quantities the following,

$z_{ref} = H$ layer demiheight

$$t_{ref} = H^2 \gamma_w m_v/k \qquad (8)$$

$u_{ref} = u_o$

to have the new dimensionless variables $U = u/u_{ref}$, $Z = z/z_{ref}$, $T = t/t_{ref}$.
By means of the relations (8), equations (6) and (7) become

$$U_T = \{ a(\frac{k_o}{k}) + b[\frac{\varkappa}{k}(-1)^{\lambda-1} \frac{\lambda |U_Z|^{\lambda-1}}{(\frac{\gamma_w}{u_o} H)^{\lambda-1}}]\} U_{ZZ}$$

$$\text{if } i \leq i_e \qquad (9)$$

$$U_T = U_{ZZ} \qquad \text{if } i > i_e \qquad (10)$$

subject to the conditions

$$U(0,Z) = 1$$
$$U(T,0) = 0$$
$$U(T,2) = 0$$

Going on to the finite differences |6| eqn.s (9) and (10) become, at the generic grid point Z_i of the layer:

$$U_i^{n+1} = U_i^n + \frac{\Delta T}{\Delta Z^2}\{ a(\frac{k_o}{k}) + b[(-1)^{\lambda-1}\frac{\varkappa\lambda}{k} \frac{|U_{i+1}^n - U_{i-1}^n|^{\lambda-1}}{(2\Delta Z \frac{\gamma_w}{u_o} H)^{\lambda-1}}]\} (U_{i+1}^n - 2U_i^n + U_{i-1}^n) \qquad \text{if } i \leq i_e$$

$$U_i^{n+1} = U_i^n + \frac{\Delta T}{\Delta Z^2}(U_{i+1}^n - 2U_i^n + U_{i-1}^n) \quad \text{if } i > i_e$$

where ΔT is the time integration step and $\Delta Z = Z_{i+1} - Z_i$ (assumed constant for this application) the space integration step.

RESULTS

A wide range of soils has been numerically explored and compared with classic Terzaghi's results.

A layer of soil 2 meters thick has been considered, subject to three different values of initial excess pore pressure (1960, 980 and 490 kPa). For different values of i_o and i_e (with $i_e = 2\, i_o$ for simplicity), and k_o and k, the results obtained are reported in tables A,B,C. These tables contain the values of the average consolidation degree for values of the time factor T equal to 0.1, 0.5, 1, 5, 10, where:

$$\bar{U} = 1 - \frac{1}{2}\int_0^2 U\, dZ$$

Table A,B,C: **Values of mean degree of consolidation $\bar{U}$ for different conditions**

CASE A

	$i_o = 1.6$			$i_e = 3.2$		
	$K = 1 \cdot 10^{-11}$ m/sec			$K = 5 \cdot 10^{-11}$ m/sec		
T \ u_o	490 kPa	980	1960	490	980	1960
0.1	0.331	0.344	0.351	0.331	0.344	0.351
0.5	0.656	0.710	0.737	0.656	0.710	0.737
1.0	0.794	0.858	0.895	0.794	0.858	0.895
5.0	0.951	0.974	0.986	0.951	0.974	0.986
10.0	0.975	0.987	0.993	0.975	0.987	0.993

CASE B

	$i_o = 0.4$			$i_e = 0.8$		
	$K = 1 \cdot 10^{-10}$ $K_o = 4 \cdot 10^{-11}$ m/sec			$K = 4 \cdot 10^{-11}$ $K_o = 1 \cdot 10^{-11}$ m/sec		
T \ u_o	490 kPa	980	1960	490	980	1960
0.1	0.349	0.353	0.356	0.347	0.351	0.355
0.5	0.728	0.739	0.759	0.703	0.736	0.759
1.0	0.885	0.905	0.918	0.867	0.896	0.913
5.0	0.998	0.999	0.999	0.991	0.994	0.997
10.0	1.000	1.000	1.000	1.000	1.000	1.000

CASE C

	$i_o = 0.2$					
	$K = 1 \cdot 10^{-9}$ $K_o = 5 \cdot 10^{-10}$ m/sec			$K = 5 \cdot 10^{-9}$ $K_o = 2.5 \cdot 10^{-9}$ m/sec		
T \ u_o	490 kPa	980	1960	490	980	1960
0.1	0.354	0.356	0.357	0.354	0.356	0.357
0.5	0.743	0.759	0.764	0.743	0.759	0.764
1.0	0.910	0.921	0.927	0.910	0.921	0.927
5.0	0.999	1.000	1.000	0.999	1.000	1.000
10.000	1.000	1.000	1.000	1.000	1.000	1.000

For clays (case A) nqteworthy discrepances can be deduced between numerical and classic results; such dicrepancies are more marked with the lowering of the value of u_o. Instead, the permeability coefficient variation does not affect the consolidation process (as one can olearly observe from the equations).

Almost the same behavior can be observed for silts and clays (case B) with regard to the interstitial initial over pressure, but a dependence of the mean consolidation degree on the ratio between the permeability coefficients k_o and k can also be noted in the sense that a slower consolidation process correponds to smaller values of k and k_o, as expected.

In the third case (C), Terzaghi's theory agrees with numerical results, and thus appears to be reliable. The computational results have been obtained for constant ratios k_o/k in both the applications shown.

CONCLUSIONS

A simple numerical study has been carried out to investigate whether new models based on empirical relations could replace Darcy's law in describing the consolidation process of soils with lowor very low coefficient of permeability such as silts and clays.

These empirical relations have been introduced into the equations, according to Terzaghi's classic theory, governing the consolidation phenomenon of a layer of soil in the case of initial excess pore pressure constant over the whole layer. In order to simulate this transitory phenomenon in a straightforward and accurate manner, a very simple explicit finite difference scheme has been used.

The numerical results obtained have shown, in accordance with physical behavior, that the consolidation phenomenon differs from Terzaghi's prediction the more the flow trend deviates from Darcy's law and the lower the initial excess pressure.

REFERENCES

|1| Terzaghi K., Theoretical Soil Mechanics, Wiley and Sons, New York, 1943.

|2| DesaiC.S., Flow through porous media, Numerical Methods in Geotechnical Engineering, Edited by C.S. Desai and J.T. Christian, Mc Graw-Hill, New York, 1977.

|3| Nendza H., Gabener H.G., Flow phenomena in soils with small permeability, Proceedings of the 11th International Conference on Soil Mechanics and Foundation Engineering, vol. 2, pp. 597-602, San Francisco, 1985.

|4| Gabener H.G., Untersuchungen uber die Anfangsgradienten und Filtergesetze bei bindingen Boden, Bulletins of the Foudation Engineering and Soil Mechanics Section of the University of Essen vol. 6, Essen, 1983.

|5| Hansbo S., Consolidation of clay with special reference to influence of vertical sand drains, Swedish Geotechnical Institute Proceedings n. 18, Stockholm, 1960.

|6| Carnahan B., Luther H.A., Wilkes J.O., Applied Numerical Methods, John Wiley & Sons Editing, New York, 1969.

Numerical Methods in Geomechanics (Innsbruck 1988), Swoboda (ed.)
© 1989 Balkema, Rotterdam. ISBN 90 6191 809 X

Distributions of stresses and strain-rates in snowpacks

H.-P.Bader, H.U.Gubler & B.Salm
Swiss Federal Institute for Snow and Avalanche Research, Weissfluhjoch, Davos, Switzerland

ABSTRACT: 2- and 3-dimensional model calculations for the distribution of stresses and deformations in a snowpack in function of external and internal parameters are performed. A linear viscous constitutive equation is assumed. The computations are based on the finite element and/or the boundary element method. The results are compared with field-measurements of stresses and deformations in new snow.

1. INTRODUCTION

The investigation of stresses and deformations in a realistic snow cover is of theoretical and practical importance for several reasons:

i) concerning the stability of a snowpack with regard to possible release of avalanches

ii) for the planning and optimizing of supporting structures to control and prevent avalanches

iii) to find criterions for the stabilazation effect of mountain forests in function of the density of trees and other parameters

iv) to gain insight into the mechanism of avalanche release.

In the past, several methods to measure the stresses and strains in a snowpack were investigated and applied: the snow pressure and deformation gauge method, the creep angle method, the holemark method and others. They are described in detail in refs.[1],[2] and refs. therein. All these measurements were performed in old snow and in the neutral zone. However, no results are available for new snow.

Theoretically, in view of ii) above, some analytical solutions for an simplified infinite snow cover (i.e. approximated governing equations) perturbed by a rigid wall are known. As boundary conditions vanishing velocity as well as gliding on the wall and the ground were considered. (For ref. see [1],[2] and refs. therein)

In the last 15 years, such problems were also solved numerically, mostly by the finite element method. Besides these "wall-problems", stress distributions were also determined for infinite curved layered snowpacks by Curtis et. al. [3]. (See also refs. in [1],[2])

All these studies were only in 2 dimensions and for special sets of parameters.

Our aim is to study theoretically and experimentally the influence on the stresses and deformation-rates in a snow-pack of:

a) external parameters: slope geometry, surface roughness, rigid obstacles like walls, trees, rocks etc.

b) internal parameters: viscosity and density, boundary conditions, interface conditions between different layers etc.

We are mainly interested in layers of new snow and in conclusions in view of i)-iv) above.

2. MODELS AND SIMULATIONMETHODS

2.1 Governing Equations

Since we consider only slowly moving dry snowpacks, the following approximations are not too restrictive: (see also [2])

1) Neglection of the kinetic energy terms

2) infinitesimal strain rates

3) a linear viscous constitutive equation

For simplicity we choose a cartesian coordinate system. So we do not have to distinguish between covariant and contravariant components of tensorfields, which is necessary in general coordinate systems. Under these assumptions the governing equations are as follows:

$$\sigma_{ij,j} + \rho F_i = 0 \qquad (1)$$

(conservation of momentum)

$$\sigma_{ij} = 2\mu[\dot{\epsilon}_{ij} + \dot{\epsilon}_{kk}\,\delta_{ij}\,/(m-2)] \qquad (2)$$

(constitutive equation)

$$\dot{\epsilon}_{ij} = 0.5[v_{i,j} + v_{j,i}] \qquad (3)$$

where:

- σ_{ij} : components of the stress tensor
- F_i : specific body forces (gravitat.)
- ρ : density
- $\dot{\epsilon}_{ij}$: comp. of the strain rate tensor
- v_i : velocity
- μ : viscosity
- m : inverse of the viscous analogue of Poisson's ratio
- δ_{ij} : Kronecker symbol
- $_{,j}$: partial derivative with respect to coordinate x_j

In all the equations we use Einstein's summation convention

2.2 Boundary conditions (b.c.)

We assume linear boundary conditions of the following type on the boundary of the domain: ($\vec{x}$: point on the boundary)

$$M_{ij}(\vec{x})v_j(\vec{x}) + R_{ij}(\vec{x})p_j(\vec{x}) = w_i(\vec{x}) \qquad (4)$$

M_{ij}, R_{ij}: components of tensor fields defined on the boundary depending on the actual boundary condition

$p_i = \sigma_{ij}n_j$: stress vector

n_i : outward normal vector on the boundary

w_i : given vector field on the boundary

The equation (4) is a covariant formulation of the boundary conditions and includes all the cases we are intersted in. For instance Newtonian viscous friction in 2 dimensions applied for simple shearing with a boundary layer thickness δ is as follows:

$$\begin{pmatrix}1 & 0\\ 0 & 1\end{pmatrix}\begin{pmatrix}v_1\\ v_2\end{pmatrix} + \begin{pmatrix}-1/\mu_r & 0\\ 0 & 0\end{pmatrix}\begin{pmatrix}p_1\\ p_2\end{pmatrix} = \begin{pmatrix}0\\ 0\end{pmatrix}$$

$\mu_r = \mu_o/\delta$

μ_o : viscosity of the boundary layer

Equations (1)-(4) describe a linear boundary value problem.

2.3. Numerical Methodes:

As is well known, analytical solutions for the boundary value problem above exist only in cases with simple domains and boundary conditions. Therefore it is generally necessary to solve them numerically. We used two different approaches : the finite element method as a local method and the boundary element method as a global technique. Since these procedures are described in numerous textbooks and papers, let us say only a few words about these methodes.

a) Boundary element method: (BEM) the method described by Brebbia et al. [4] was generalised to include the more general boundary conditions (4). The gravitational force was taken into account by either superimposing a particular inhomogenic analytical solution or by transforming the body force domain-integrals into boundary-integrals using the Galerkin-tensor as described in ref. [5]. Finally the discretised integral equation was solved using Gauss-elimination with partial pivot-selection. The programm code developped applies to 2-dimensional plane-strain or plane-stress problems with constant elements.

b) Finite element method: (FEM) we used the finite element programm TPS10. this programm applies to 2 and 3 dimensions, linear and nonlinear constitutive equations and various types of constant and linear elements.

All numerical calculations were performed on a 32-bit Hewlett-Packard HP330 computer.

2.4. Scaling properties of the solutions

By scaling, it is possible to extend solutions found for special sets of parameters to other sets. It can easily be shown that if $\tilde{v}_i, \tilde{\sigma}_{ij}$ is a solution of (1)-(4) with parameters $\tilde{\rho}, \tilde{\mu}$, m and b.c. $\tilde{M}_{ij}, \tilde{R}_{ij}, \tilde{w}_i$, then

$$v_i = \tilde{v}_i \cdot H^2 \cdot \frac{\tilde{\mu}}{\mu}\frac{\rho}{\tilde{\rho}} \qquad (5a)$$
$$\sigma_{ij} = \tilde{\sigma}_{ij} H \frac{\rho}{\tilde{\rho}}$$

is a solution of (1)-(4) with parameters ρ,μ,m and b.c.

$$M_{ij} = \tilde{M}_{ij} \cdot \frac{\mu}{\tilde{\mu} \cdot H}$$

$$R_{ij} = \tilde{R}_{ij} \qquad (5b)$$

$$w_i = \tilde{w}_i \cdot H \cdot \frac{\rho}{\tilde{\rho}}$$

in a domain extended by a factor H. It is exactly this scaling property that allows to generalize results found by studying special cases as done in section 4.

3. EXPERIMENTS

Here we describe the idea only very briefly. In a subsequent paper they will be discussed in more detail. With a platform of size 0.5m*0.5m with several pressure sensors, normal as well as shear stresses were measured in the interface between two layers of snow. To measure the velocity of deformation the lower part of the platform was fixed to the lower layer whereas the upper part moved with the upper layer of snow. Measurements were performed in a snowpack around some trees. A first analysis of the results showed no contradiction to the results obtained by the calculations.

4. RESULTS AND DISCUSSION

We present results of two problems in snowmechanics. The first is the so-called "wall-problem" where a rigid wall interrupts the movement of the snow cover as shown in Fig.1 and the second is the "tree-problem" where the wall in Fig.1 is replaced by a stem of a tree.

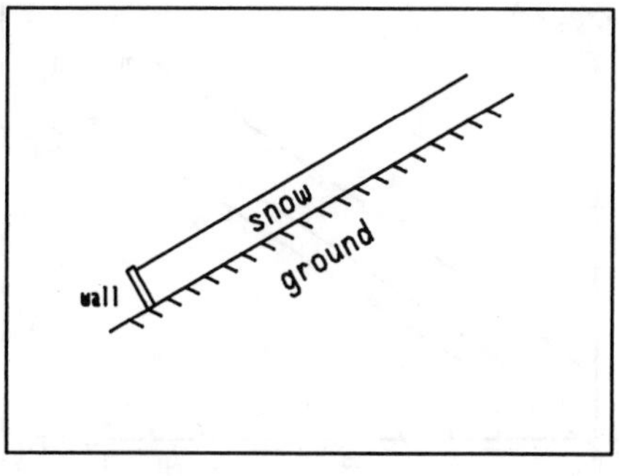

Fig.1 "wall-problem": a rigid wall in the snow cover, compensating part of the snow forces

The "wall-problem" was treated with the BEM as a 2-dimensional plane-strain and the "tree-problem" as a truly 3-dimensional problem with FEM. The stresses and deformation velocities were calculated in function of the various parameters. In particular we are interested in 2 characteristic features of the stress/strain distributions:

a) the force F acting on the wall/tree

b) the length x_b of the back pressure zone which is defined as follows: it is the distance on the surface of the snow from the obstacle to a point where the component of the velocity parallel to the ground has reached 95% of its undisturbed magnitude.

The parameters ρ,μ and the thickness D of the snow cover were fixed to typical values:

$$\rho = 100 \text{kg/m}^3$$
$$\mu = 10^9 \text{ N sec/m}^2$$
$$D = 1\text{m}$$

This is no restriction since with (5) the results can be extended to other values of ρ,μ and D.

The other parameters: m, slope angle ψ and the b.c. on the ground and the wall were varied.

4.1 "Wall-problems"

Results of a typical BEM-calculation are presented in Fig.2-5. Fig.2 shows the discretisation of the structure with smaller elements on the wall and nearby. Fig.3 and 4 present parallel and normal components of stresses on the wall and velocities on the snow surface respec-, tively. Fig.5 finally gives the principal stresses in the neighborhood of the wall. Let us now discuss the results. First we assume vanishing velocity on the wall and on the ground.

i) slope angle:

as demonstrated in Table 1 and Fig.6 the back pressure zone is almost independent of the slope angle and the total force on the wall is a linear function in $\sin\psi$. Since $\rho g D^2 \sin\psi$ is the total shear stress of a portion of the snowpack with a size D*D, the quantity $F/(\rho g D^2 \sin\psi)$ represents the number of such portions whose total shear stress is compensated by the forces on the wall.

For the slope angle 30° in Fig.3 the stress distribution on the wall is approximately symmetric with respect to the middle of the wall. For larger slope angles (50°) the stresses are more concentrated on the upper part and for smaller slope angles ($<=15^o$) more concentrated on the lower part of the wall. These facts can be explained as follows. There are 2 contributions to the force on the wall. First, the settlement (proportional to $\cos\psi$) induces sidewards forces which increase with increasing settlement, i.e. these forces are larger in the lower part of the wall. Second, the weight component parallel to the ground (proportional to $\sin\psi$) is larger in the upper part of the wall since in the lower regions it is compensated partly by the shear forces on the ground because of the boundary conditions. Thus for small slope angles the first contribution and for large slope angles the second contribution dominates.

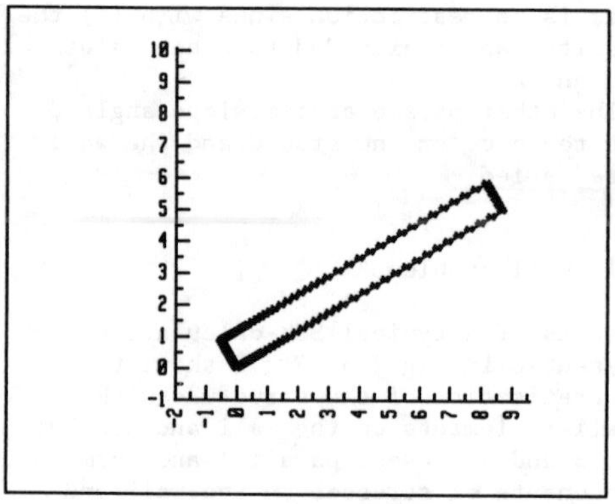

Fig.2 BEM-discretisation of a typical "wall problem"

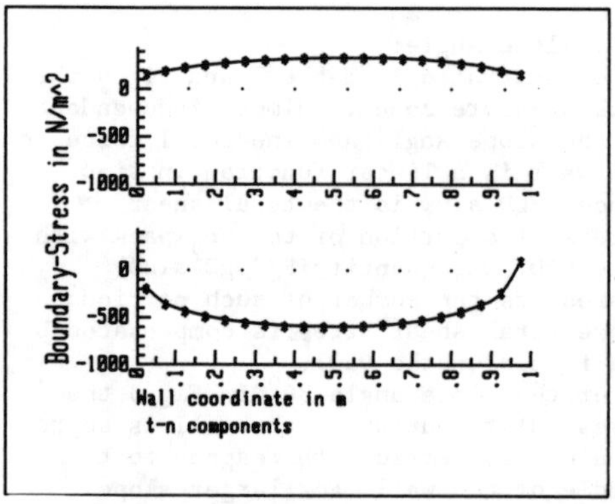

Fig.3 Parallel and normal components of the stress on the wall

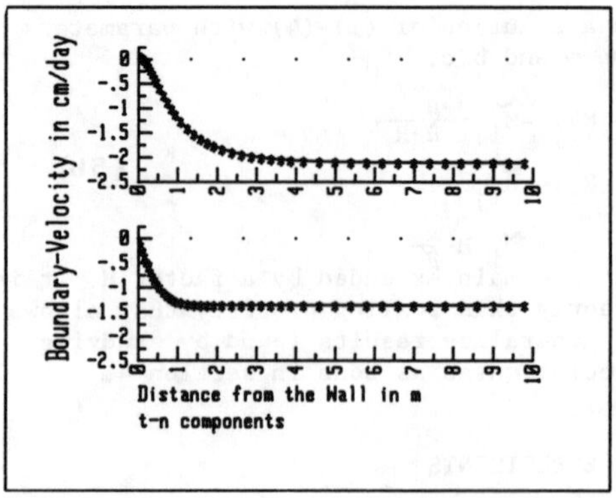

Fig.4 Parallel and normal components of the velocity on the surface of the snoe cover

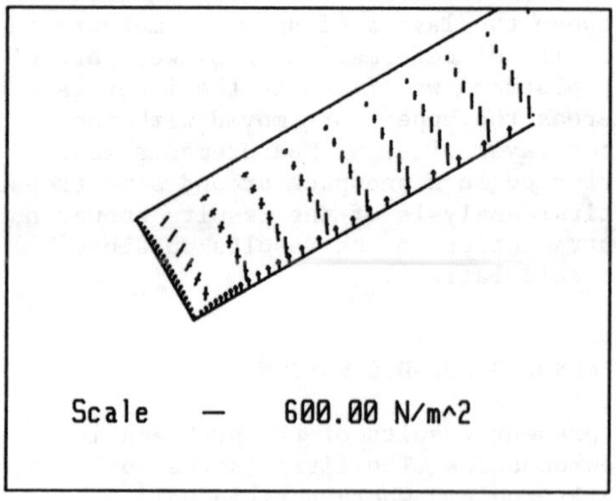

Fig.5 Principal stresses and reacting forces of the ground and the wall

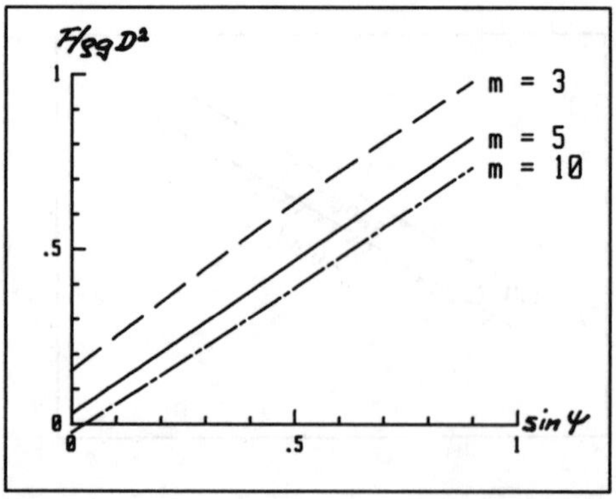

Fig.6 Normalized normal component $F/(\rho g D^2)$ of the force on the wall in function of slope anlge ψ for three values of m

ii) influence of m:
as also shown by table 1 and Fig.6 the more compressible i.e. the higher m (m=2 incompressible m=∞ compressible) the smaller the back pressure zone and the forces on the wall. This can also be explained by the decreasing sidewards action of the settlement with increasing m. This sidewards pressure can even be so small that the resultant force on the wall is negative: for m=10 and $\psi=0^o$ see Fig.6.

Table 1. Back pressure zone (meter) in function of ψ and m

ψ	15°	30°	45°
m=3	3.4	3.5	3.5
m=5	3.1	3.1	3.1
m=10	2.9	2.9	2.8

iii) influence of boundary conditions:
Fig.7 and 8 demonstrate the dependence of x_b and F in function of the gliding velocity or the friction coefficient on the ground. Here we assume a Newtonian friction law:

$\tau = -\mu_r v_\parallel$ where

τ : shear stress

$v_\parallel$: parallel component of the velocity

Of course both, x_b and F increase with increasing gliding velocity. The point $\mu/(D\mu_r)=1$ corresponds to about a gliding velocity of two times the surface velocity with no gliding. Experimentally gliding up to $\mu/(D\mu_r) \approx 3$ was observed. The qualitative features i) and ii) above remain true if gliding occurs. Approximatively x_b and F in function of the friction coefficient can be described by the following formulas:

$$x_b/D = 3+2.6\cdot(\mu/(\mu_r D))^{0.72}$$

$$F/(\rho g D^2 \sin\psi)=0.88+1.15\cdot(\mu/(\mu_r D))^{.59}$$

or:

$$x_b/D = 3+0.72\cdot(N^2-1)^{0.72}$$

$$F/(\rho g D^2 \sin\psi)=0.88+0.4\cdot(N^2-1)^{0.59}$$

where N is the gliding factor.
These "thumb rules" which deviate less than ±5% from the curves in Fig.7,8 can be useful for the practice.

iv) comparision to other solutions:
For all previous solutions (see ref.[1]) the stresses on the wall in function of the wall coordinate differ up to a factor 2 from the BEM-solution. However the integrated quantities like total force or torque differ only up to 10-15% from the BEM-solution. This is the effect of the integration procedure which sometimes smoothes out large deviations.

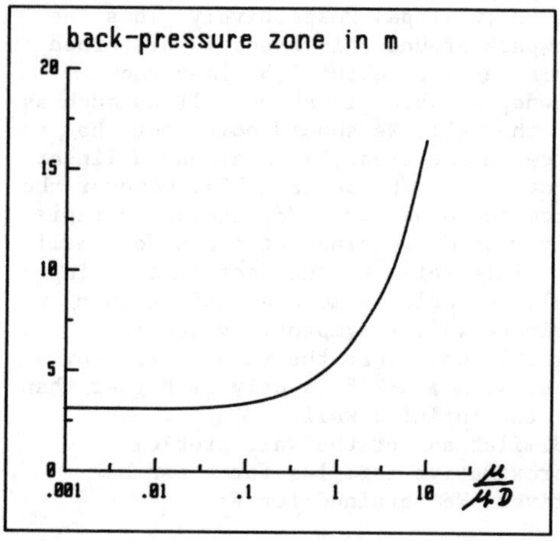

Fig.7 Length of the back pressure zone in function of the coeff. of friction μ_r

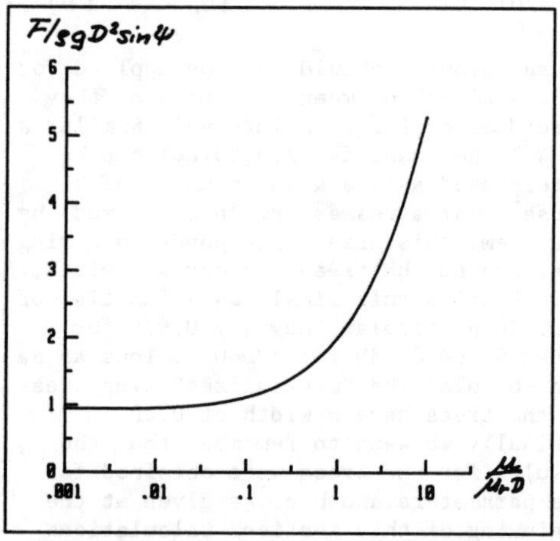

Fig.8 Normalized normal component $F/(\rho g D^2 \sin\psi)$ of the force on the wall in function of the coeff. of friction μ_r

4.2 "tree-problems"

Similar as in section 4.1 we calculated the back pressure zone and the force on the tree in function of the ratio ϕ/D where ϕ is the diameter of the stem. We chose m=5, $\psi=30^{\circ}$ and ρ,μ and D as given at the beginning of section 4. No gliding on the ground and the stem was allowed. The results are presented in Fig.9 and 10.

With decreasing ratio ϕ/D of course also x_b and F decrease. The values of x_b for very thin stems are $\approx$D (sidewards) and $\approx$1.5D (upslope) respectively. Thus the snowpack around thin trees is disturbed in a ring area of about 1.5 times the snowdepth, which is about half as much as for the wall. We should point out that the force on the tree (F) is almost a linear function in ϕ/D (see Fig.10). However the force per diameter (F/ϕ) increases rapidely with decreasing ratio ϕ/D for small ϕ/D. This reflects the fact that a single small obstacle is more efficient than an infinite wall (asymptotic value in Fig.10). Note that the value (F/ϕ) for trees with ϕ/D=2.5 is only 5% higher than for the infinite wall.

Similar as for the wall-problem approximative formulas for F can be derived. We obtained for F:

$$F=\rho g D^3 \sin\psi(0.85+2.68(\phi/D)-0.14(\phi/D)^2)$$

and for F/ϕ:

$$\frac{F}{(\phi/D)}=\rho g D^3 \sin\psi\left(2.34+1.04\left(\frac{\phi}{D}\right)^{-1}-0.022\left(\frac{\phi}{D}\right)^{-2}\right)$$

These formulas should only be applied for values of ϕ/D between 0.1 and 3 as they were derived for this interval. Similar as in 4.1 the quantity $F/(\rho g D \sin\psi)$ can be interpreted as the area in units of D^2 whose shear stresses are "neutralized" by the stem. This area corresponds to a ring area around the tree of a certain width, which varies only slowly as a function of ϕ/D. In particular they are 0.67D for ϕ/D=2.5 and 0.53D for ϕ/D=0.1. Thus as a "thumb-rule" the "neutralized" ring areas of the trees have a width of 0.6D.

Finally we want to remember that the results for the trees were obtained for the parameters and b.c. as given at the beginning of this section. Calculations for other parameters and b.c are in current progress, where also the effect of densification will be taken into account.

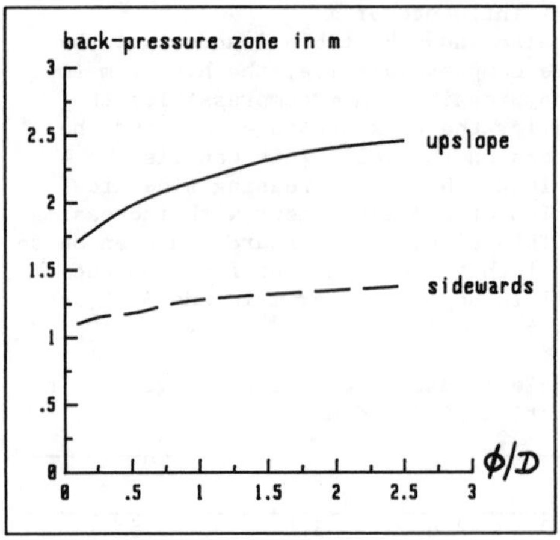

Fig.9 Length of back pressure zone in function of the ratio ϕ/D for trees in sidewards and upwards direction

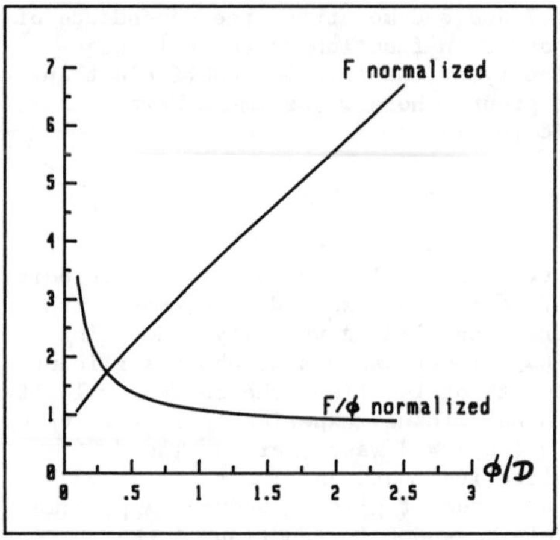

Fig.10 Normalized component parallel to the ground of the force $F/(\rho g D^3 \sin\psi)$ and the force per peripheral meter $F/(\rho g D^3 \sin\psi\ \pi\phi)$ in function of the ratio ϕ/D

ACKNOWLEDGEMENT

It is a pleasure to thank P.Weilenmann for his helpful contributions to the computer codes.

REFERENCES

[1] B.Salm,Snow forces, Journ.Glaciol.19, 67-100 (1977)
[2] M.Oh'izumi,Determination of stresses in the snow cover on a mountain slope by snow pressure gauge,Contr.Ser.A 35, 55-97 (1986) Inst.Low.Temp.Sci.Hokkaido Univ.
[3] J.O.Curtis,F.W.Smith,Material property and boundary condition effects on stresses in avalanche snow-packs,J.Glaciol.13, 99-108 (1974)
[4] C.A.Brebbia,The Boundary Element Method for engineers, Pentech Press 1980
[5] C.A.Brebbia,J.C.F.Telles,L.C.Wrobel, Boundary element Techniques: Theory and Application, Springer Verlag 1984

Numerical Methods in Geomechanics (Innsbruck 1988), Swoboda (ed.)
 ISBN 90 6191 809 X

The boundary condition study on the BEM applying to the slope analysis

Guangzhong Sun, Xiaoning Wang & Zhuhua Liu
Institute of Geology, Academia Sinica, Beijing, People's Republic of China

ABSTRACT: On the basis of computing results, two types of BEM model applying to slopes are discussed. In the end of paper, an example of selecting correct model for the slope is presented.

1 INTRODUCTION

It is believed that we should firstly determine how to select the BEM model correctly before applications. In order tp do this, one of the most important is to select the boundary conditions correctly. This paper mainly studies the effects of the boundary condition on the computing results of the BEM models of slopes. During the computing it is supposed that the slope is homogenous, contineous, isotropical and plan stress state in elastical extent.

2 STUDY OF BOUNDARY CONDITIONS

The binding types of the common computing models may be divided into two types (Fig.1).

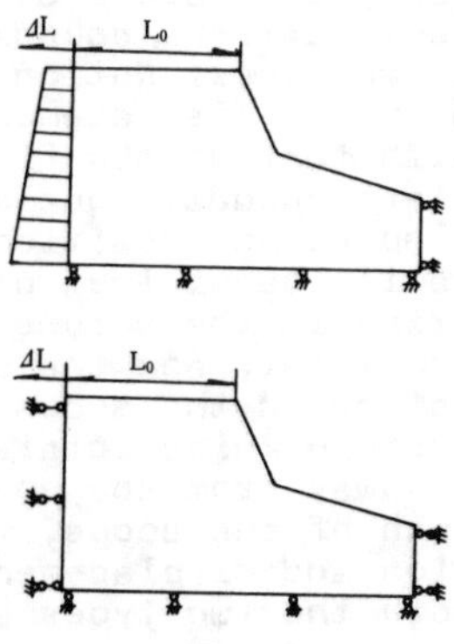

Fig.1 Sketch of two binding types.

2.1 The first binding type

The main boundary conditions of this type are computing scope, boundary force and the relative size of the computing scope. Various circumstances of boundary conditions have been considered. From the computing results of BEM, it is known that the stress and displacement in the slope are entirely different with the gradual increment of the slope's gradient. In most cases, when the slope is horizontal, the direction of the displacements in the slope is downward. But as the gradient of the slope becomes larger, the directions of the displacements change upward. The increments of stresses and displacements are directly proportional to the increment of the boundary force (Fig.2,3). This shows that this type of computing model is similar to the cantilever beam when the gradient increases to some level. The larger the boundary force of the left boundary, the more evident the effect of the cantilever beam. When the gradient exceeds the level, this computing model loses its effectiveness.

In order to remove the cantilever beam effect, the computing scope of the left boundary may be extended so as to increse the bending stiffness of the model. Fig.4,5 show when the scope extends left to some level, the cantilever beam effect apparently decreases. But it is worth paying attention that for different point, the decreased degree

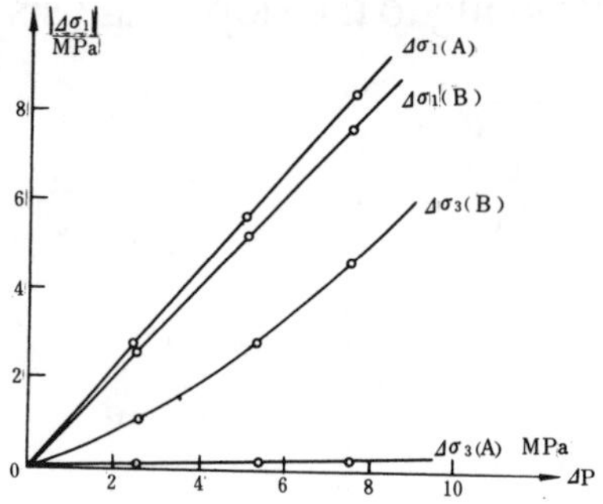

Fig. 2 Relations of boundary force increment and stress increment at point A & B in slope.

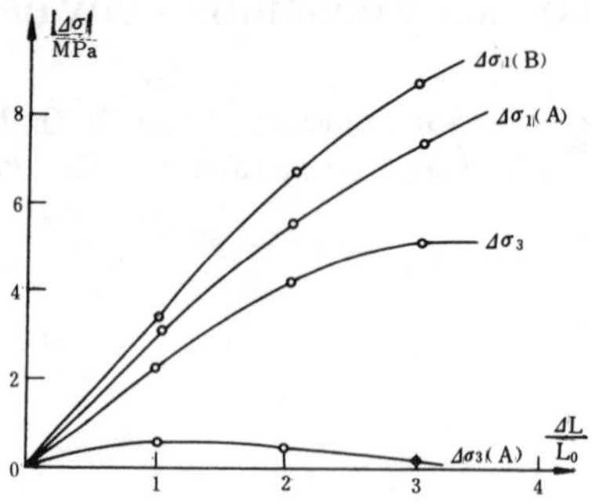

Fig.4 Curves of stress increments at point A & B in slope when scope extended.

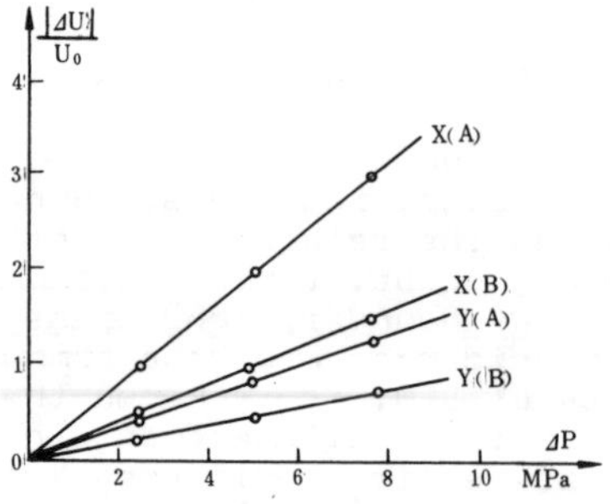

Fig.3 Relations of boundary force increment and displacement increment at point A & B in slope.

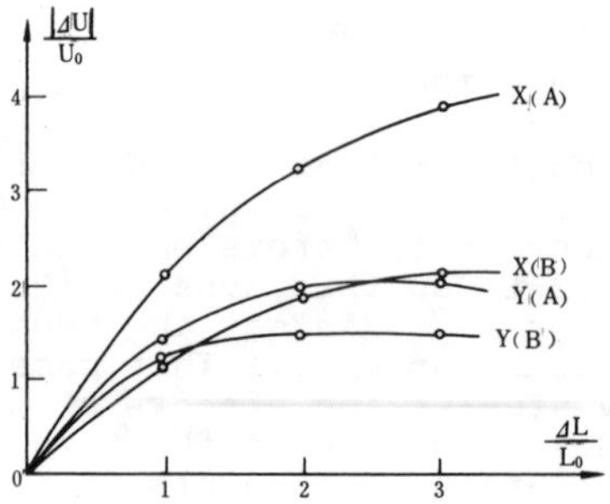

Fig.5 Curves of displacement increments at point A & B in slope when scope extended.

is different, generally the interior points change less apparently than the points near to boundary.

2.2 The second binding type

This type is different from the first binding type, the effect of the boundary force has been removed here. The main boundary conditions are the shape of the slope and the relative size of the computing scope. The computing results at different computing scopes have been attained to. Fig.6,7 are two examples. We may know from the results that there is a large difference for the stress direction near to the boundary between this binding type and the first one. The direction of the maximum main stress for the first type is nearly horizontal. But for the second one, it closes to be vertical near the boundary or makes an angle larger than 45° with the horizontal axis. This doesn't accord with the actual situation because the side compress factor used in computation is larger than one. As to the computing results for the displacement, they are also entirely different near the boundary between the two types. Not only the direction of the displacement is inverse with that of the first type near the left boundary,but also the maximum displacement position in the first type is the minimum displacement position in the second type as viewed from total, and the displacement direction in the second type has the anticlockwise rotatal tendency. Far away from the boundary in the depth of the scope, the stress direction and displacement direction of both the two types are nearly the same.
The above results show that the different scope of the BEM computing

model may be selected according to the different boundary conditions. Under the first binding type, when the gradient of the slope becomes steeper and the boundary force is larger, the computing model is then similar to the cantilever beam; when the computing scope in the horizontal direction is extended to some level, the computing model is then similar to the pressed bar model under the multi-binding; when the size of the slope is increased monotonously in the horizontal and vertical directions, the computing model becomes a plate only forced vertically. For the second binding type, the computing model then becomes the pressed bar model under the multi-binding with the increment of the gradient and the height of the slope, but the direction of the pressed bar is inverse with the first type. If the size increased monotonously in the horizontal and vertical directions at the same time, this computing model then becomes the plate bound in three sides and freed in one side

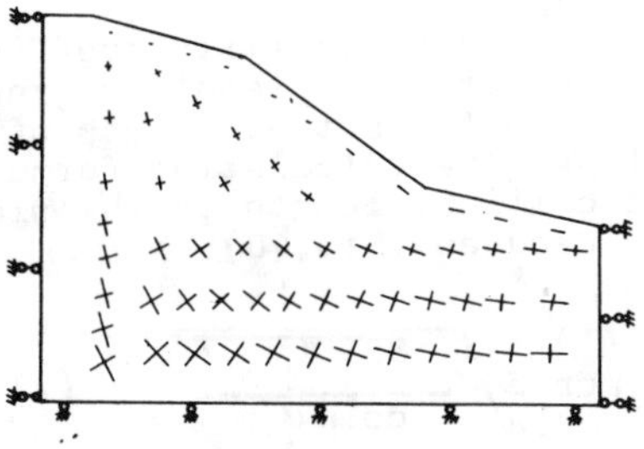

Fig.6 Stress distribution of the second binding type.

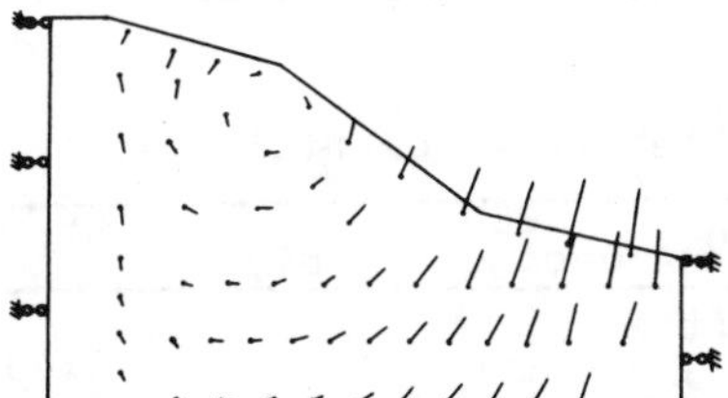

Fig.7 Displacement distribution of the second binding type.

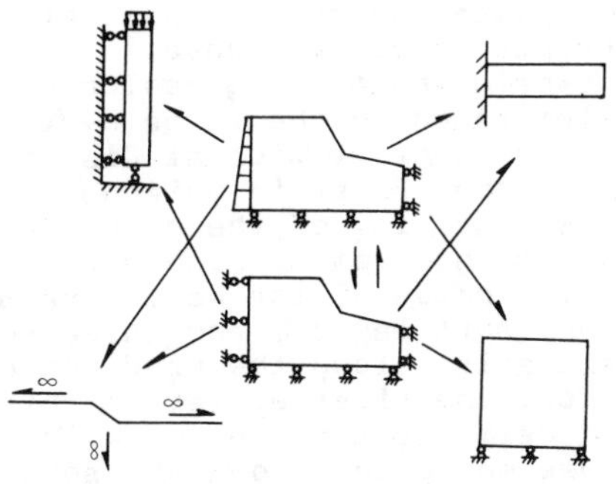

Fig.8 Interrelations among the computing models.

Moreover, if the two kinds of the binding model detailed above extend limitlessly in two directions and in the vertical direction, the computing model becomes the model of the half-infinite body (Fig. 8).

3 EXAMPLE OF APPLICATION

That the computing models of the slopes affect the computing results has been studied under different boundary conditions. It is believed that any type of the computing models is an approximation and can't completely model the actual slope in the slope engineerings. The half-infinite body model closes mostly to the actual situation, if seen from theoretical view. But the computing scope is too large and the computing method has become to infinite element method(IEM).

Therefore the computing model of BEM can be determined according to the stress characteristics, gradient, height of the slope and the goal of the computation. If the main goal is to compute the stress in the slope, the first type of the binding model is better; and if the displacement, then the second. If the stress and displacement of the slope are to be computed at the same time, then the computing scope and model should be selected fitly according to the magnitude of the stress, gradient and height, etc. of the slope, and the effects of the boundary conditions on the computing results should be reduced as possible or be removed. It is better to use the IEM of the half-infinite body if possible. The following is the example of the application on the basis of the principle described above.

The main engineering geological problem faced to the large hydroelectric power station at Qianshenqiao, Nanpan River in Guizhou, China, is the stability of the high slope. There is the typical high slope with the alternates of the hard layers and the soft layers, and three soft layers exist along the gradient direction. The first writer of this paper believes that the buckling failure may occur along the soft layers when the base of the slope is digged, although the slope is in stable state at this moment.

The buckling failure is one type of the slope losing its stability, which exists in the rock slopes possessing the slab-rent constructure especially in the southwestern region of China. Generally, following three basic requirements should be satisfied for the occurance of buckling failure:

1. the rock layers and the soft interlayers along the gradient direction;
2. relatively high slope and relatively steep gradient;
3. evident stress concentration or tension stress at the base of the slope.

The Qianshenqiao slope is entirely satisfied with the first and second requirements. Therefore in order to analysis the probablity to occure the buckling failure for this slope, we should put emphasis on analysing the stress of the slope.

According to the principles concluded above, the first computing model is selected, and according to the magnitude of the stress measured at the site and the height of the slope, the proper computing model is selected. The distribution of the stress by the BEM is shown in Fig.9. We may know from the computing result that the rock probably yields at the base of the slope and the buckling failure may be resulted in because the tension stress occures at the base of the slope after it is digged.

Based on the first writer's theoretical deluction for the buckling failure, the stability of the slope may be detected by following formula.

$$K=\frac{Lcr}{L} \qquad (1)$$

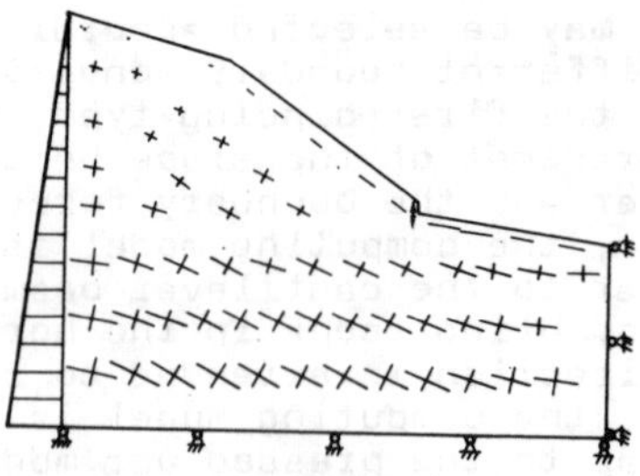

Fig.9 Stress distribution in Qianshenqiao slope when digged.

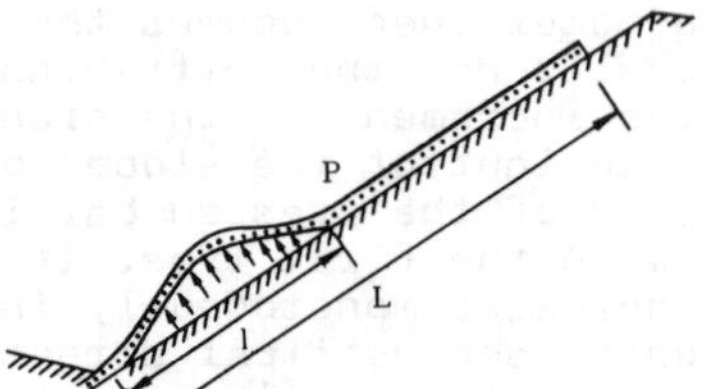

Fig.10 Mechanical model of slabrent rock mass in slope.

Where, K is the stability coeffient; Lcr is the critical length of the slope; L is the actual length of the slope. The calculating formula of the critical length of the slope may be deduced (Fig.10):

$$Lcr=3\sqrt{\frac{8EI\pi^2}{q\sin\alpha}} \qquad (2)$$

Where, E is the elastic coefficient; I is the bending stiffness; q is the weight per univolume of rock; α is the gradient of the slope.

According to the formulas (1) and (2), the stability coefficients of Qianshenqiao high slope is shown in Tab.1.

Tab.1 Stability coefficients.

Section	BC undig.	BC dig.	CE
Fir.soft layer			3.00
Sec.soft layer			3.69
Trd.soft layer	1.06	0.92	3.51

The geological sketch of Qianshenqiao slope is shown in Fig.11. From the Tab.1 it is known that the slope probably will have the buckling failure only in the section BC, so this part should be reinforced.

4 CONCLUSIONS

Above analyses may led following conclusions:

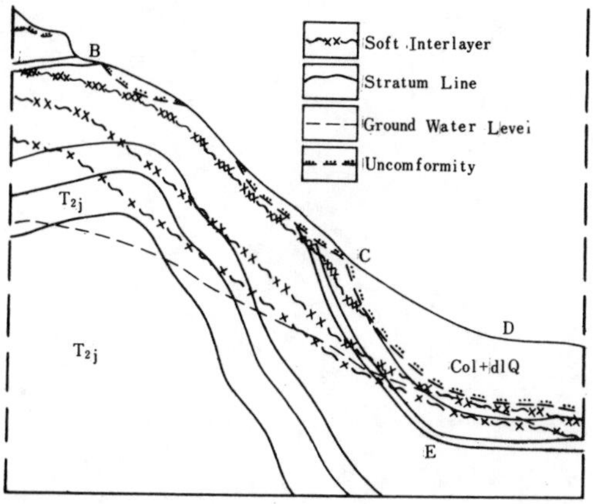

Fig.11 Geological sketch of Qianshenqiao slope.

a. Applying BEM to compute the stress and displacement of the slope has the characteristics of the rapidity, convenience and takes less computing time.

b. The boundary conditions evidently affect the results of the BEM. The first binding type is fitter for computing the stress of the slope; and the second for the displacement. But no matter which model, the effects of the boundary binding should be removed when we apply the computing results.

c. The first binding type may become the cantilever beam, the pressed bar with the multi-binding and the plate forced only in the length-ways direction under the conditions of the different gradient, height and computing scope etc. The second binding type may also become the pressed bar with the multi-binding and the plate bound in three sides and freed in one side. If above two types of the models extend limitlessly in directions and in the vertical direction, then they become the IEM model of half-infinite body.

d. Based on above principles, the probability of the buckling failure in Qianshenqiao high slope with soft-interlayers has been analyzed. The results have proved the correctness and suitability of the principles.

REFERENCES

(1) S.L. Crouch and A.M.Starfield, Boundary Element Method in Solid Mechanics, George Allen & Unwin Pub. Ltd., London, 1983.

(2) J.C.F. Telles, The Boundary Element method applied to inelastic problems, Spring-verlag Berlin Heidelberg, 1973.

(3) Sun Guanzhong and Zhang Wenbin, A Commonly-sighted Rock Mass Structure —— Slab-rent Structure and its Mechanical Model. Scientia Geologica Sinica, No. 3, 275-282, 1985.

Numerical Methods in Geomechanics (Innsbruck 1988), Swoboda (ed.)
© 1989 Balkema, Rotterdam. ISBN 90 6191 809 X

Three dimensional stability analysis of the tunnel face under fluid pressure

M.Mohkam & Y.W.Wong
Ecole Nationale des Travaux Publics de l'Etat, Vaulx-en-Velin, France

ABSTRACT : A three dimensional mathématical approachbased on limiting équilibrium state combined with variational method is used for stability analysis of the tunnel face under fluide pressure. On one hand, 3D slip surface (log-spirals) is much closer to the reality and on the other hand arching effect and different mechanical parameters of soil as well as rheological properties of the slurry are taken into consideration. More-over, different types of mud cakes are accounted for. The numerical analysis show the influence of the different mechanical parameters of soil as well as the type of mud cakes on 3D stability analysis and the pressure to be applied at the tunnel face. In comparison with 2D analysis, the pressure is smaller in 3D. The difference is more important for soils presenting some cohesion, for deeper tunnels and specially for smaller diameters. Finally results are compared to some in field datas and show good agreement.

1 INTRODUCTION

In slurry shieldmethod the pressure applied to the tunnel face equalizes, in theory, the existing earth and hydrostatic pressures. Hence, equilibrium of the tunnel face is obtained and, besides, no changes occur in the state of stress. However, the pressure applied should be carefully calculated. If it is too large, it results upheaval, or if it is too small, excessive settlements on surface, and/or failure could occur. A review of different methods in practice shows that the choice of the pressure is made normally through simple calculations. In general, the pressure to be applied is the sum of "assumed" earth pressure at rest and existing hydrostatic pressure plus a safety pressure which is some 20 or 30 k Pa. [1], [2], [3]. Or it is found by two dimensional analysis of moment equilibrium of acting forces [4]. Meanwhile, these methods don't take into consideration mechanical properties of soil and rheological characteristics of the slurry used. More-over, it is assumed that the pressure is completely mobilized at tunnel face. Whereas, in reality, this assumption is not true in all cases. As a function of the type of mud cake, the pressure is completely mobilized in the case of a membrane formation in finer soils, or partially mobilized in the case of a rheological blocking in coarser soils.

In followings first we define sources of stability which should be taken into consideration in stability analysis, then mathematical approach is described. Some numerical analysis are made and the results presented are finally compared to some in field experiences.

2 SOURCES OF STABILITY OF THE TUNNEL FACE UNDER SLURRY PRESSURE

2.1 Mud cake formation

Figure 2.1 shows schematic view of the pressure chambre at frontal part of a slurry shield.

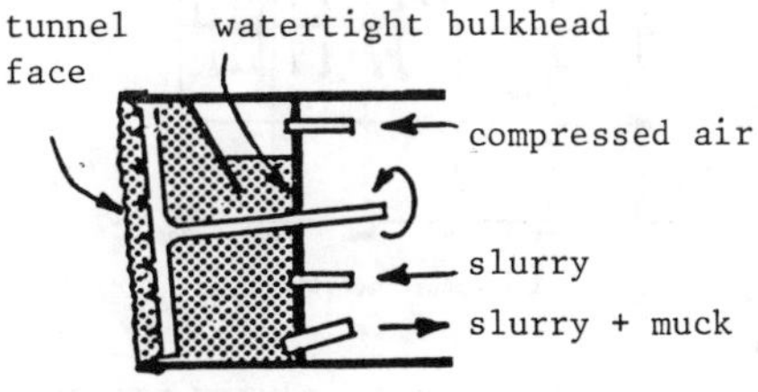

Fig. 2.1 Slurry shield pressure chambre scheme

Slurry under air pressure penetrates the soil at tunnel face and fills in the voids over a certain depth and formes the so called "mud cake". The mud cake formed then mobilizes the pressure applied in the slurry and supports the face.

The depth of penetration and quality of mud cake depend on the rheological properties of slurry, pressure applied and on the physical characteristics and hydrogeological conditions of the ground excavated [5] , [6] .

In general three types of mud cake formation could be expected [6] , [7] :

a) Membrane cake in fine sandy soils as a thin layer of sustensions retained on tunnel face ;

b) Impregnation cake in gravel soils with high permeability ;

c) Mixed cake, partly impregnated into sandy gravel soils combined with a membrane cake which we call [8] over-cake,up-stream of impregnation cake.

2.2 Pressure Gradient

Mobilisation of slurry pressure at tunnel face varies based on the type of mud cake formation. It could be completly mobilized in case of a membrane cake within which pressure gradient is very high. Or it could be partially mobilized in case of impregnation and mixed cakes, since amplitude of the pressure gradient depends on the width of the cakes which in this case is relativly large. Experimental studies conducted at the Geomateriaux Laboratory of E.N.T.P.E. have lead into development of non-dimensional curves indicating pressure gradients in sandy, sandy gravel and gravel soils (figures 2.2 et 2.3)

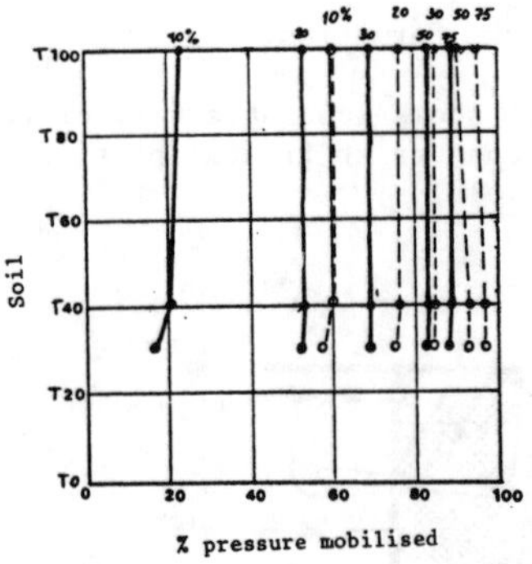

Fig. 2.2 Mobilisation of slurry pressure (%) in sandy gravel soils over different fractions of cake width

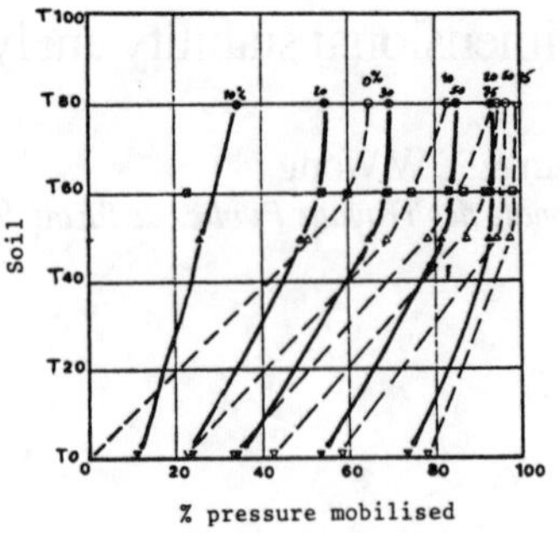

Fig. 2.3 Mobilisation of slurry pressure (%) in coarse gravel soils over different fractions of cake width

Where, the absciss a represents soils containing different percentages of grains finer than 5 mm and the ordinate indicates differet percentages of slurry pressure mobilised.

It is to note that the pressure gradient within the cake is non-linear and that two régimes are stablished :

- Transitory régime (solid curves) when formed cake is destructed by the shield and ;
- Stationary régime (dashed curves) when after a lapse of a few seconds a new cake is formed.

3 FORMULATION AND MATHEMATICAL APPROACH

3.1 Assimilation of the problem

In order to simplify the problem, tunnel face is assimilated to a verticale slope undergoing the loads shown in figure 3.1.

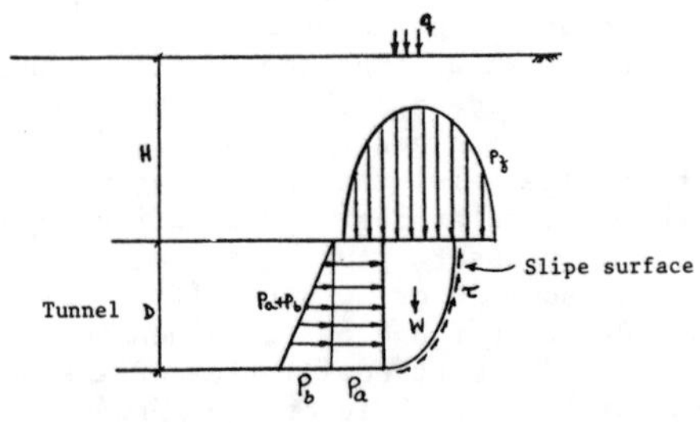

Fig. 3.1 Loads acting on the potential sliding wedge at tunnel face

Where q = surcharge
P_z = overburden pressure
P_a = air pressure
P_b = slurry pressure distribution
w = weight of the sliding wedge
τ = shear resistance of soil along slip surface given by

Mohr Coulomb Law $\tau = C + (\sigma - u)\ tg\ \phi$

Overburden pressure P_z is calculated based on the concept of the arching effect of soil and the loosened ground pressure. Terzaghi's formula is used to determine the height h_a of arching (fig. 3.2) :

$$h_a = \frac{B(1-2C/\gamma B)}{2Ktg\,\phi}\left(1-e^{-2Ktg\phi\, H/B}\right) + \frac{G}{\gamma} e^{-2Ktg\phi\, H/B} \qquad (3.1)$$

Hence, P_z is given by (3.2) :

$$P_z = \gamma' h_a \qquad (3.2)$$

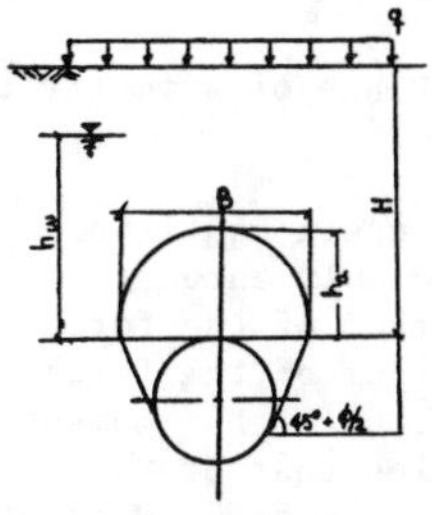

Fig. 3.2

Where ϕ = Internal friction angle of soil
γ = Bulk density of soil
γ' = Effective Bulk density
C = Cohesion
k = Ratio of horizontal to vertical earth pressure

3.2 Basic approach

The procedure is the same as presented by [9]

A mass of soil bounded in between slope surface $Z(x,y)$ and the slip surface $z(x,y)$ is considered in equilibrium state when the following conditions are satisfied :

a) Failure criteria ; $\tau = f(\sigma)$ (in this case $\tau = c + \sigma_n\ tg\phi$)
where $\tau(x,y)$ and $\sigma(x,y)$ are respectivly the distribution of the shear resistance and the normal stress along the slip surface $z(x,y)$;

b) Equilibrium equations ;

c) Extremization of a fonctional H with respect to 3 unknown functions $z(x,y)$, $\sigma(x,y)$ and $\theta(x,y)$, where $\theta(x,y)$ represents slip direction projected on x-y plane.

$$H_{ex} = H_{z,\sigma,\theta}[z(x,y), \sigma(x,y), \theta(x,y)] \qquad (3.3)$$

In order to simplify the formulation, vectorial presentation is used (fig. 3.3)

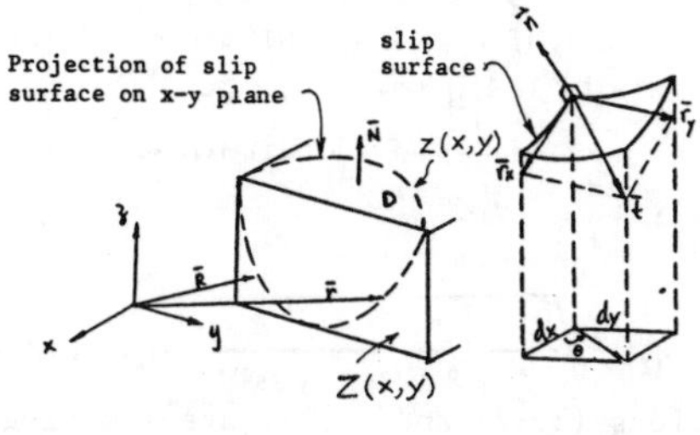

Fig. 3.3 Conventions in vectorial presentation of 3D analysis

Then the equilibrium equations are written as follows :

resultant force f =

$$\int_D\int \left[\sigma\bar{n} + \tau|\bar{n}|\frac{\bar{t}}{|\bar{t}|} - \gamma(\bar{R} - \bar{r}) + \bar{P}|\bar{N}|\right] dxdy = 0 \qquad (3.4)$$

resultant moment m =

$$\int_D\int \left\{\bar{r} \times \left[\sigma\bar{n} + \tau|\bar{n}|\frac{\bar{t}}{|\bar{t}|} - \gamma(\bar{R} - \bar{r})\right] + [\bar{R} \times \bar{P}]|\bar{N}|\right\} dxdy = 0 \qquad (3.5)$$

where : $\bar{R}$ is the radius vector representing points on the slope surface ;

$$\bar{R} = x\bar{i} + y\bar{j} + Z(x,y)\bar{k} \qquad (3.6)$$

$\bar{r}$ is the radius vector representing points on the slip surface ;

$$\bar{r} = x\bar{i} + y\bar{j} + z(x,y)\bar{k} \qquad (3.7)$$

$\bar{N}$ is the vector normal to the slope surface ;

$$\bar{N} = \bar{R}x \times \bar{R}y = -Zx\bar{i} - Zy\bar{j} + \bar{k} \qquad (3.8)$$

$\bar{n}$ is the vector normal to the slip surface ;

$$\bar{n} = \bar{r}x \times \bar{r}y = -zx\bar{i} - zy\bar{j} + \bar{k} \qquad (3.9)$$

$\bar{t}$ is the vector tangent to the slip surface;

$$\bar{t} = -(\bar{r}x + \bar{r}y\ tg\ \theta) \qquad (3.10)$$

$\bar{P}$ is external force acting on the slope surface and $\gamma = \gamma(x,y)$ is the average unit weight of the sliding wedge. In the limiting equilibrium state the shear resistance mobilised is given by :

$$\tau_m = [C + (\sigma - u)\psi] / F \qquad (3.11)$$

where F is a safety factor, $C = C(x,y,z)$ is the effective cohesion, $\psi = \psi(x,y,z) = tg\ \phi$ and $U = U(x,y,z)$ is the pore water pressure.

Substituting (3.11) into (3.4) and (3.5) results in :

$$f^{*} = \int_D\int \{ \left|\frac{\bar{n}}{\bar{t}}\right| [c + (\sigma - u)\psi]\, \bar{t} - F\, [\gamma\, (\bar{R} - \bar{r}) - \sigma \bar{n} - \bar{P}\, |\bar{N}|]\}\, dxdy = 0 \tag{3.12}$$

$$m^{*} = \int_D\int \{\bar{r} \times \left|\frac{\bar{n}}{\bar{t}}\right| [c + (\sigma - u)\psi]\, \bar{t} - F\, [\gamma\, (\bar{R} - \bar{r}) - \sigma\bar{n} - \bar{P}\, |\bar{N}|]\}\, dxdy = 0 \tag{3.13}$$

where : $f^{*} = F.f$
$m^{*} = F.m$

and;

$$\frac{|\bar{n}|}{|\bar{t}|} = \sqrt{\frac{1 + z^{2} + z^{2}}{1 + tg^{2}\theta + (z_x + z_y\, tg\theta)^{2}}} \tag{3.14}$$

Equations (3.12) and (3.13) are limiting-equilibrium ones and depend on unknown parameter F and three functions z (x,y), σ(x,y) and θ (x,y). However any one of the six equations could be solved for F to obtain un explicit relation between F and the three unknown functions :

$$F = \tilde{F}\, [z(x,y),\ \sigma(x,y),\ \theta(x,y)] \tag{3.15}$$

Problem of limiting equilibrium is then to find three functions z (x,y), σ (x,y) and θ (x,y) which give the minimum value Fs of the functional $\tilde{F}$ and satisfy all six equations of limiting equilibrium, therefore :

$$F_s = \min_{z,\sigma,\theta}\ \tilde{F}\, [z(x,y),\ \sigma(x,y),\ \theta(x,y)] \tag{3.16}$$

subject to the satisfaction ot

$$f^{*}\, [z(x,y),\ \sigma(x,y),\ \theta(x,y),\ F] = m^{*}\, [z(x,y),\ \sigma(x,y),\ \theta(x,y),\ F] = 0 \tag{3.17}$$

3.3 Variational analysis

Equations (3.16) and (3.17) define a variational problem, solution of which is the same as the solution of isoparametic problem.

An auxiliary functional H {z (x,y), σ(x,y), θ(x,y)} is to be minimized where H is defined as

$$H = \bar{\lambda}\, .\, \bar{I} + \bar{\mu}\, \bar{J} = 0 \tag{3.18}$$

$\bar{I}$ and $\bar{J}$ are same as f^{*} and m^{*} except that F is replaced by its minimum Fs. λ and μ are Lagrange's multipliers

$$\bar{\lambda} = \lambda^{x}\bar{i} + \lambda^{y}\bar{j} + \lambda^{z}\bar{k} \tag{3.19}$$

$$\bar{\mu} = \mu^{x}\bar{i} + \mu^{y}\bar{j} + \mu^{z}\bar{k} \tag{3.20}$$

Functional H could be written as

$$H = \int_D\int h\, dxdy \tag{3.21}$$

where

$$h = \bar{\lambda}\, \{\frac{|\bar{n}|}{|\bar{t}|} [c + (\sigma - u)\, \psi]\bar{t} - F_s[\gamma(\bar{R} - \bar{r}) - \sigma\bar{n} - \bar{P}\, |\bar{N}|]\} + \bar{\mu}\, \{\frac{|\bar{n}|}{|\bar{t}|} [c + (\sigma - u)\psi](\bar{r} \times \bar{t}) - F_s\, [\gamma(\bar{r} \times (\bar{R} - \bar{r})) - \sigma(\bar{r} \times \bar{n}) - \sigma(\bar{r} \times \bar{n}) - (\bar{R} \times \bar{r})\, |\bar{N}|]\} \tag{3.22}$$

In the case of tunnel, symmetry exists (fig. 3.4). The x - z plane is chosen as the symmetry plane. Hence, equilibrium of the force in y-direction and equilibrium of the moment with respect to x and z-axes are automatically satisfied.

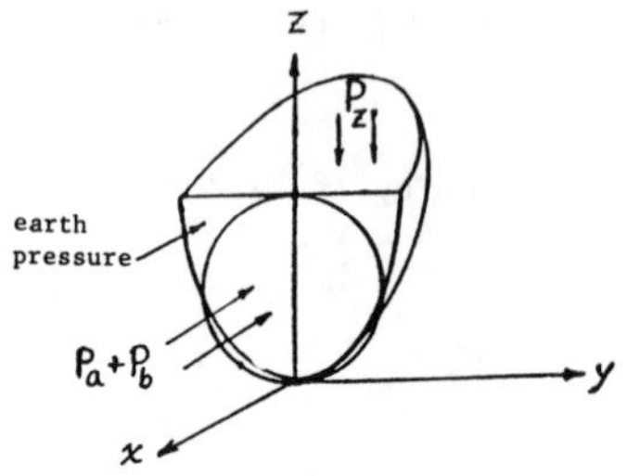

Figure 3.4 - Plane of symmetry in tunnel

There-fore, the six equilibrium equations are reduced to only three :

1-equilibrium of the force in x-direction;
2-equilibrium of the force in z-direction;
3-equilibrium of the moment about y-axis

This implies that Lagrange's multipliers λ^{y}, μ^{x} and μ^{z} are zero. Hence the function h is defined as

$$h = [c + (\sigma - u)\psi]\, (|\bar{n}|\, /\, |\bar{t}|)\{1 + \lambda^{z}(z_x + z_y\, tg\, \theta) + \mu^{y}\, [z - x(z_x + z_y\, tg\, \theta)]\} - Fs\, \{\sigma[z_x - \lambda^{z} + \mu^{y}\, (x + z.z_x)] + \gamma\, (Z - z)(\lambda^{z} - \mu^{y}x)\} - Fs\, \{p^{x} + \lambda^{z}\, p^{z} + \mu^{y}(p^{x}Z - p^{z}x)\}\, [1 + Z^{2}x + Zy^{2}]^{1/2} \tag{3.23}$$

where P^{x} and P^{z} are the distribution of the forces respectivly in x and z directions.

Application of the first and the second Euler's equations [10] to the function h yields

$$tg\, \theta = \frac{z_y(\lambda^{z} - \mu^{y}x) - z_x\, z_y(1 + \mu^{y}z)}{z_x(\lambda^{z} - \mu^{y}x) + (\mu^{y}z + 1) + z_y^{2}(1 + \mu^{y}z)} \tag{3.24}$$

$$(1 + 1/\psi^{2}m)[(1 + \mu^{y}z)zx - (\lambda^{z} - \mu^{y}x)]^{2} - (zx^{2} + zy^{2} + 1)[(1 + \mu^{y}z)^{2} + (\lambda^{z} - \mu^{y}x)^{2}] = 0 \tag{3.25}$$

The solution of the partial differential equation (3.25) is the potential slip surface z(x,y).

Remark 1 : As demonstrated first in 2D problems [1] and then in 3D problems [9] it is to note that the determination of the slip surface and consequently the factor of safety Fs is independent of the normal stress distribution along the slip surface.

In order to simplify the partial differential equation (3.25), coordinate system is first translated to a new cartesian system (fig. 3.5a) and then transformed to a spherical coordinate system (fig.3.5b)

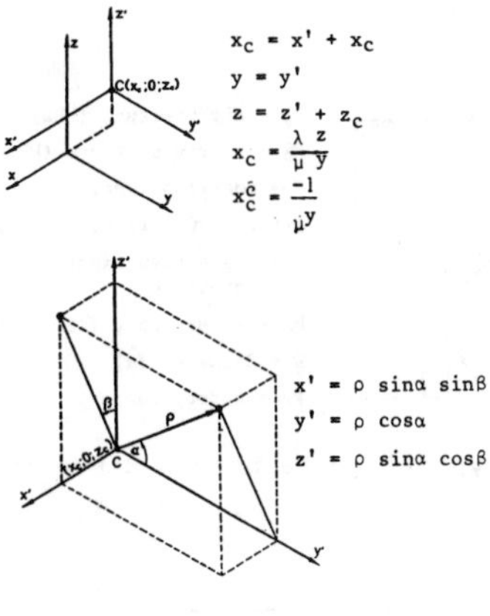

Fig. 3.5 Transformations of the coordinate system

In the new system, equation (3.25) yields two solutions :

$$\rho = Ae^{-\psi m \beta} \sin \alpha \qquad (3.26)$$

and;
$$\rho = Ae^{-\psi m \beta} / \sin \alpha \qquad (3.27)$$

where A is a constant.

Figure 3.6 Shows graphicalrepresentation of (3.26). The half of the symmetrical surface shown indicates that the solution has 3D characteristics. Whereas (3.27) represents an infinite cylindrical surface with 2D characteristics there-fore excluded.

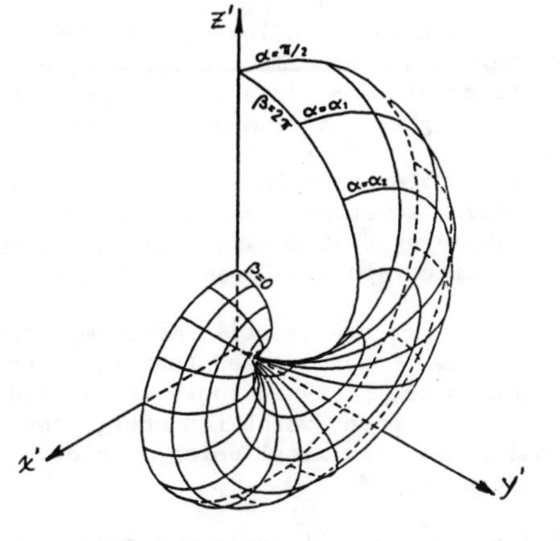

Fig. 3.6 Graphical representation of equation (3.26)

Remark 2 : In order that the slip surface be admissible the limits of α and β are

$$\frac{\pi}{4} < \alpha < \frac{3\pi}{4} \qquad (3.28)$$

$$\pi < \beta < \frac{3\pi}{2} \qquad (3.29)$$

In the new cartesian system equation (3.23) is defined as

$$h = [c + (\sigma-u)\psi] \{[(z-z_c) + z_x(x_c - x)]^2 + z_y^2 [(z-z_c) + (x_c-x)^2]\}^{1/2} + Fs\gamma(Z-z)(x_c-x) + Fs\sigma[(x-x_c) + z_x(z-z_c)] + Fs[P^x(z_c-z) - p^z(x_c-x)](1+Zx^2+Zy^2)^{1/2} \qquad (3.30)$$

The functional H becomes

$$H = \int_D\int h\,dxdy = 0 \qquad (3.31)$$

The safety factor Fs is given as follows

$$F_s = \left\{ \frac{\int_D\int [c+(\sigma-u)\psi]\{[(z-z_c)+z_x(x_c-x)]^2 + z_y^2[(z-z_c)^2+(x_c-x)^2]\}^{1/2}\,dxdy}{\int_D\int \gamma[(Z-z)(x-x_c)] - \sigma[(x-x_c)+z_x(z-z_c)] - [p^x(z_c-Z)-p^z(x_c-x)](1+Zx^2+Zy^2)^{1/2}\,dxdy} \right\} \qquad (3.32)$$

3.4 Solution procedure

The safety factor and the potential slip surface are determined respectivly by (3.32) and (3.26). The four unknowns in these equations are y_c, z_c, A and Fs. If a point on the potential slip surface, center of the spiral (x_c, 0, z_c) and a safety factor value are known the slip surface is obtained and the safety factor Fs is calculated by iteration of (3.32). A point at the foot of sliding wedge is considered known and an initial value is given to F. The flow chart given in figure 3.7 shows the procedure.

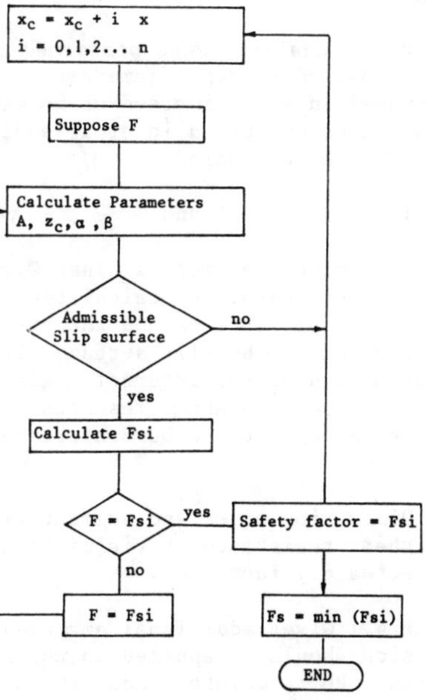

Fig. 3.7 Flow chart of the solution procedure

3.5 Consideration of the type of mud cake in the problem

As mentioned in chapter 2 pressure mobilization at tunnel face varies as function of the type of mud cake and the pressure gradient developed.

Figure 3.8 Shows determination of the mobilized pressure P_{xm} and its distribution against sliding wedge according to the pressure gradient developed within the mud cake.

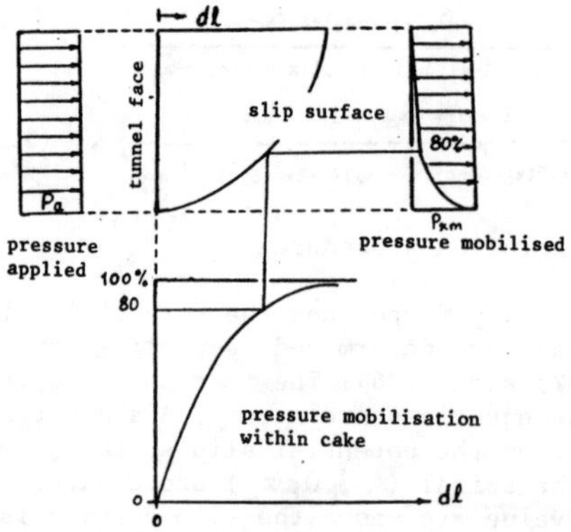

Fig. 3.8 Determination of mobilized pressure at tunnel face

4. RESULTS

Numerical analyses were performed for some cases, where different diameters and depths of tunnel in soils imersed or not with various cohesions C and internal angles of friction were studied.

4.1 Influences of C and Ø

The mechanical parameters C and Ø of the soils affect both, the calculation of the overburden pressure Pz and the shear resistance along the slip surface. If the cohesion and/or the internal angle of friction increase shear resistance τ increases also, but overburden pressure Pz decreases.

Diminution of Pz and augmentation of the shear resistance τ yields then a higher safety factor Fs.

Table 4.1 Gives additional air pressure Pa which should be applied to the slurry pressure Pb to maintain equilibrium state of the tunnel face (Fs = 1).

Figure 4.1. Shows the general configuration of the tunnel and definition of the terms used here on.

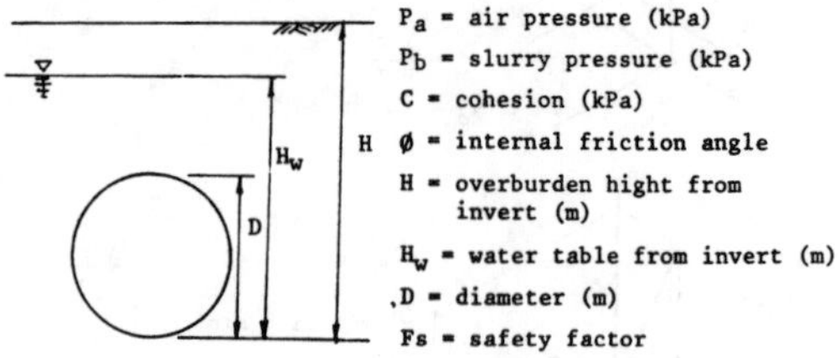

Fig. 4.1 Typical geotechnical x-section of tunnel

C \ Ø	30	20	10	0
0	22	54		
10	0	31		
20	0	7	51	
30		0	20	103
40			0	54
50				38

H = 28 m, $\frac{Hw}{H} = 1$, D = 8 m, Fs = 1

Table 4.1 Necessary air pressure to be applied

4.2 Comparison of 2D and 3D analyses

Tables 4.2 a and b indicate, respectivly for imersed and non-imersed tunnels, pressure Pa obtained by 2D and 3D analyses for the limiting equilibrium of the tunnel face.

It is noted that in all cases 3D analysis gives lower pressure Pa than 2D analysis implying that 2D analysis yields to conservative values of pressure to be applied.

The difference is still more important in the case of non-imersed tunnel, where, in some cases, pressure could be reduced by 75 kPa, a point which for energy consumption and economical point of view is considerable.

4.3 Influence of different mud cakes

Figure 4.2 shows an idealized pressure gradient within an impregnation cake formed over 2.5 m from tunnel face. It is to be noted that 70 % of the pressure applied is mobilized at one meter distance and 100 % at 2.5 meters

Analysis \ Ø	35	30	25	20
2D	28	39	53	73
3D	10	21	34	53

C = 0
H = 28 m
$\frac{Hw}{H} = 1$
D = 8 m
Fs = 1

4.2a)

Analysis \ Ø	35	30	25	20
2D	57	72	100	137
3D	0	0	23	62

C = 0
H = 28 m
$\frac{Hw}{H} = 0$
D = 8 m
Fs = !

4.2b)

Table 4.2 Necessary air pressure Pa from 2D and 3D analyses for the care of : a) imersed tunnel and ; b) non-imersed tunnel

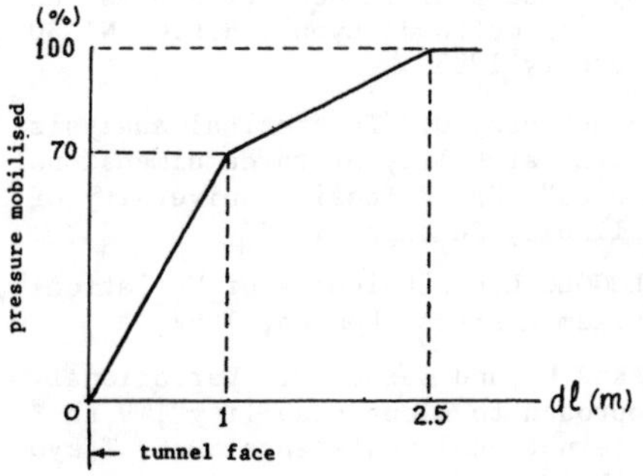

Fig. 4.2 Idealized pressure gradient within impregnation cake

Table 4.3 shows, for different diameters of tunnel, the safety factors Fs in the cases of the membrane and impregnation cakes

Cake \ D	10	8	6
Membrane	1.28	1.48	1.78
Impregnation	1.16	1.33	1.47

C = 0
Ø = 35°
Pa = 30kPa
H-D = 10 m
$\frac{Hw-D}{H-D} = 1$

Table 4.3 Safety factor in cases of different mud cakes

It can be seen that the safety factor, comparing to the case of membrane cake, is smaller in the case of impregnation cake.

Graphical representation of the safety factor values of table 4.3 shows clearly (fig. 4.3) that the difference of the safety factors between the two cases becomes larger for smaller tunnel diameters.

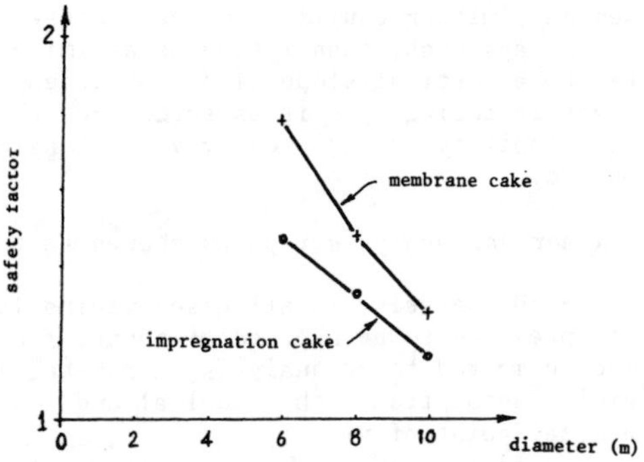

Fig. 4.3 Influence of the different cakes on safety factor

4.4 Comparaison with some in-field datas

The ratio of $\frac{Lx}{D}$, (fig. 4.4) in the numerous numerical analyses performed is found to be between 0.4 and 0.6.

Where Lx is the distance of the slip surface to the tunnel face at the crown, and D is tunnel diameter.

In practice actuel values of the ratio was found [7] to have a mean value of 0.55 (fig. 4.4). Hence, results of 3D analysis show a good agreement with experience.

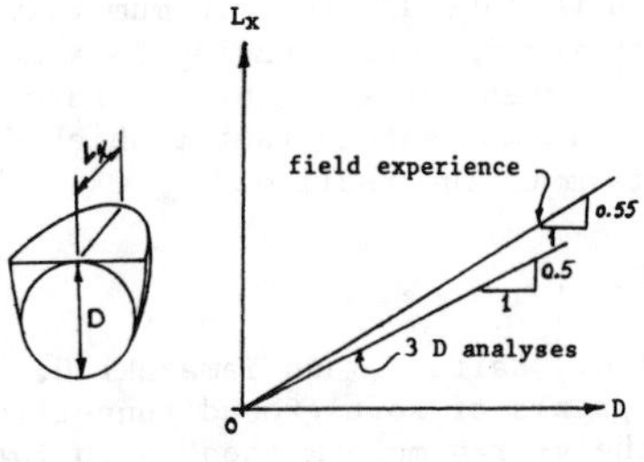

Fig. 4.4 Comparison of the ratio $\frac{Lx}{D}$ between field experience and 3D numerical analyses.

5. CONCLUSION

Simple methods and 2D analyses actually employed for stability analysis and for the choice of slurry pressure to be applied in shield tunnelling are not quite adequate. Therefore, a 3D mathematical approach based on limiting equilibrium was proposed. In the approach, tunnel face is assimilated to a vertical slope with overburden pressure acting upon it as surcharge, then its stability is analysed by variational method.

Numerical analysis results showed that :

- 3D analysis, in all cases yields lower pressure to be applied at tunnel face when compared to 2D analysis, a non-negligible factor from both technical and economical point of view ;
- As the consequence of different pressure mobilisation,the safety factor for the same pressure applied is, in impregnation type of mud cake, lower than in membrane cake. The difference is remarkably more important for smaller diameters;
- Mechanical parameters of soil play an important role in the 3D analysis and the validity of the variational method used depends on the Mohr Coulomb law. However, the safety factor is independent of the normal stress distribution along the slip surface;
- Concordence of results with some in field datas concerning the potential slip surface renders the proposed approach to a certain extent reliable;
- Finally it should be remarked that minimum safety factor by variational method is not necessarily "the minimum safety factor". On the other hand, the potential slip surface which yields the minimum safety factor is not necessarilly the realistic one. Therefore, it is more justified to consider the minimum value of safety factor corresponding to a more realistic potential slip surface rather than the minimum safety factor which does not conform to the reality.

REFERENCES :

[1] MIKI G., Saito T. and Yamazaki H. "Theory and praxis of soft ground tunnelling by the slurry mole method" 9 th International conference of SMFE, Tokyo, July 1977

[2] Yamazaki H. "Problems of the slurry shield method and their counter measures" 2nd Australian Tunnelling Conference, Melborn 1976

[3] Kumai F., Inoue M. "Mud shield tunnelling for the Hikawadi section of the subway n° 8 TRTA", Tekken Co. Ltd., Tokyo, May 1982

[4] Takahasi H. and Yamazaki H. "Slurry shield method in Japan", Proceedings of RETC, Las Vegas, June 1976

[5] Mohkam M. Bouyat C. "Research studies for slurry shield tunnelling", Proceedings of the 4th International Symposium IMM Brighton, March 1985

[6] Mohkam M., Bouyat C. "Dispositif de simulation d'un bouclier à pression de boue", International Congrès AFTES, Lyon November 1984

[7] Yamazaki H. "Stability of tunnel face and control of excavation in mud shield tunnelling", Ph. D Thesis, Tokyo, December 1982

[8] Bouyat C., Mohkam M., Morcrette J.P. "Le soutènement liquide : une recherche appliquée pour le boulier à pression de boue du métro de Lyon", R.F.G. N° 30 February 1985

[9] Leshchinsky D. "Theoretical analysis of the stability of three dimensional slopes", Ph. D Thesis, University of Illinois, Chicago, 1982

[10] ELOGOLC L.E. "Calculus of Variations", Pergamon Press, London, 1962

[11] BAKER R.,and Garber M. "Variational Approach to slope stability", 9 th International Conference SMFE, Tokyo July 1977

Numerical Methods in Geomechanics (Innsbruck 1988), Swoboda (ed.)
© 1989 Balkema, Rotterdam. ISBN 90 6191 809 X

The geotechnical design of pile-supported offshore platforms subjected to seismic loading

A.Di Carlo
Aquater S.p.A., S.Lorenzo in Campo, Pesaro, Italy

ABSTRACT: The design of fixed steel offshore platforms in seismic-prone areas requires the development of reliable design methods for the analysis of foundation behaviour under dynamic excitation and the evaluation of geotechnical input parameters for detailed dynamic analysis of the superstructure. In this paper a state-of-the-art procedure is illustrated which covers the more relevant aspects of this analysis. In particular, the influence of soils which can exhibit strong non-linear behaviour is carefully considered both in site response and soil-pile-structure interaction studies. To carry out this analysis, a system of computer codes was developed which couples DESRA-2 (Lee and Finn, 1978) and SPASM (Matlock et al., 1979) computer programs. This paper illustrates the main features of these two codes and provides a description of the entire computer program system.

1 INTRODUCTION

In addition to the standard investigations usually performed for the design of offshore structures, platforms which are located in seismically active areas require further studies concerning regional seismicity and dynamic behaviour of foundation soils.

Vibratory ground motions which can affect the site must be evaluated for two levels of shaking (strength and ductility levels), and dynamic laboratory tests (i.e. cyclic triaxial compression, simple shear and resonant column tests) must be performed to characterize soil behaviour under alternating loading conditions.

Both investigations are recommended by offshore rules (API, 1987; DNV, 1977) in order to achieve reliable input data for the earthquake-resistant design of offshore platforms.

Various methods have been developed in recent years for platform response analysis during seismic events, including a comprehensive model of soil, pile and superstructure. Nevertheless, they are unable to model soil-pile interaction when strong non-linear phenomena occur due to liquefaction or cyclic degradation of foundation soils. The analysis procedure presented in this paper is the result of an extensive literature review (Aquater, 1982) and is based on currently available approaches and associated computer codes, which are designed to properly consider the influence of soil non-linearity on platform response.

The suggested procedure involves two fundamental steps :

- free-field site response analysis
- soil-pile-structure interaction analysis.

The first step examines the response of the soil deposit to the input earthquake motion. Its main scope is determination of the displacement time-history in the soil layers, which is the input for the subsequent interaction analysis.

In the second step, soil-pile-structure interaction is analyzed with a single pile model and a simplified idealization of the superstructure; soil-pile coupling is modelled through nonlinear and inelastic interface elements.

This step provides geotechnical input data for the superstructure dynamic analysis such as acceleration response spectrum and time-history at the pile head level and stiffness and damping constants of piles.

2 FREE-FIELD SITE RESPONSE ANALYSIS

Several one-dimensional methods are today available for the evaluation of soil response and liquefaction potential of horizontally layered deposits shaken by vertically propagating shear waves.

In the suggested procedure, the computer code DESRA-2 (Lee and Finn, 1978) is adopted, which performs a nonlinear effective stress seismic response analysis of saturated sand deposits.

The program incorporates the effective stress model for sand liquefaction proposed by Martin, Finn and Seed (1975) and Finn, Martin and Lee (1978). This model is based on a set of constitutive laws which take into account the response of saturated sands to alternating loadings, including the generation and dissipation of pore water pressure.

Furthermore the effect of finite stiffness at the base of the deposit, with the possibility for energy to radiate back into the underlying medium, is considered by using an energy transmitting boundary.

Three main types of problems can be analyzed with DESRA-2, namely :

- dynamic response only (total stress approach);
- dynamic response including the effect of pore water pressure generated as a result of cyclic loading;
- dynamic response including generation, redistribution and dissipation of pore water pressure.

Input data required for the analysis are acceleration time-history at a depth corresponding to the base of the model, and soil parameters related to liquefaction strength and rate of pore water pressure generation, soil permeability, maximum shear modulus and maximum shear stress at zero volumetric strain for each soil layer.

It is worthwhile to note that reliable displacement time-histories can be obtained as a result of the analysis, if errors in the long period range of acceleration input record are carefully avoided. To this end the procedure proposed by Trifunac and Lee (1973) with the improvements suggested by Basili and Brady (1978) can be usefully applied for processing strong motion records.

As concerns Finn's liquefaction model, a method has been elaborated (Molenkamp and Di Carlo, 1984) by which soil parameters can be evaluated from both cyclic simple shear and cyclic triaxial compression test results. Soil constants which appear in the incremental equation of volumetric strain are adjusted in such a way that a good fit is obtained to the experimental liquefaction strength curves. Then it is expected that the model will provide a good prediction of in situ soil behaviour during seismic excitation.

It should be pointed out that this method also applies to clays, as long as reliable measurements of pore water pressure generated during laboratory cyclic tests are available. Thus, DESRA-2 can be used to predict the response of clayey soil deposits including cyclic degradation effects.

When running DESRA-2, a wide set of results is obtained for each layer of the soil profile, such as time-histories of acceleration, velocity, displacement, shear stress, shear strain, volumetric strain and power water pressure. Moreover, by processing these data, additional information are derived on liquefaction potential of the soil deposit, maximum acceleration, shear strain and shear stress versus depth, acceleration response spectra, shear stress-shear strain relation, mobilized friction angle, stress path and so on.

3 SOIL-PILE-STRUCTURE INTERACTION ANALYSIS

For the dynamic interaction analysis between soil, pile and superstructure, the method proposed by Matlock and Foo (1978) and the associated computer program SPASM (Matlock et al., 1979) is used.

The analysis is primarily concerned with the behaviour of a single pile, with particular emphasis on the soil-pile coupling, as stated before. The soil response is simulated by a series of closely spaced springs, friction sliders and dashpots which do not affect each other during motion. Therefore, this approach is based on the subgrade reaction method and can be considered as rather empirical in application. Nevertheless it is widely used in foundation engineering and in industrial approaches for the study of pile-supported offshore platforms under earthquake motion.

The pile is modeled by a discrete-element mechanical analog, each segment consisting of a rigid bar between adjacent deformable joints. Bending moments, axial forces and shear forces are transmitted across the bar. At each joint, internal and external dashpots respectively simulate the loss of energy due to inelastic internal deformation of pile material and both rate effects and radiated energy of the external supports.

Force-displacement characteristics of the soil support are expressed as curves of soil reaction per unit pile length, versus lateral pile deflection (the so-called p-y curves).

In this approach each curve results from an assemblage of elasto-plastic sub-elements which is used to represent any nonlinear-inelastic behaviour of the supports.

For each curve, besides the initial ultimate resistance and the curve shape, it is possible to specify the number of gap elements, a degradation factor and the lower-bound resistance value. When subsequent full reversals of slip occur, the ultimate resistance is reduced in such a way that the lower bound value is asymptotically approached. Gap elements simulate the formation of molding-away zones near the pile, as generally occurs in shallower soil layers.

The superstructure is modeled as an extension of the pile, by increasing the corresponding stiffness and considering rotational restraints at appropriate pile stations.

The dynamic numerical solution process is based on an implicit (Crank-Nicolson) type of numerical operator by which the equations of motion are formulated in terms of the unknown deflection at any beam station. For nonlinear-inelastic problems, solutions are obtained by a trial and adjustment procedure, using a tangent modulus iterative technique on the p-y curves.

This proposed analysis procedure is primarily concerned with the earthquake-resistant design of offshore platforms and SPASM analysis must be coupled with the one-dimensional site response analysis.

Moreover, SPASM computer program can be applied to solve other typical problems in offshore engineering, such as the response of the soil-pile-platform system to wave loading or to lateral soil movement due to mudslide motion, with or without dynamic effects.

4 DESRA-SPASM COMPUTER PROGRAM SYSTEM

The proposed analysis is carried out by means of a computer program system which couples DESRA-2 and SPASM.

Due to the features of these codes it is possible to cover almost any situation which can be encountered in designing a pile-supported offshore platform.

The program system is shown in Fig. 1. A description of each code is given in the Appendix.

The system consists of two similar sequences of routines developed for DESRA-2 and SPASM codes.

Any sequence is opened by a program which manages sets of results, stored on files, obtained with subsequent runs. Then, a routine (DISDES for DESRA and DISSPA for SPASM) retrieves and processes output data for one or more different runs at the same time and provides them in a graph form. Drawings can be produced both on plotter and Tektronix.

The main programs of the system are coupled by DESSPA code which transfers lateral ground displacements through scratch files from DESRA to SPASM.

Final results of the analysis are obtained through a computer program PIHEAD, which processes SPASM output data for the pile head station, producing the following data:

- displacement, velocity and acceleration time-histories;
- acceleration response spectrum and normalized response spectrum;
- horizontal and rotational mean elastic stiffness and equivalent mean hysteretic damping ratio of the foundation pile.

Furthermore, other important results are given for the entire pile model by DISSPA in terms of :

- displacement, shear force, bending moment and support reaction time-histories for any pile station;
- maximum values of displacement, shear and bending moment along the pile;
- displacement, shear and moment along the pile for selected time stations.

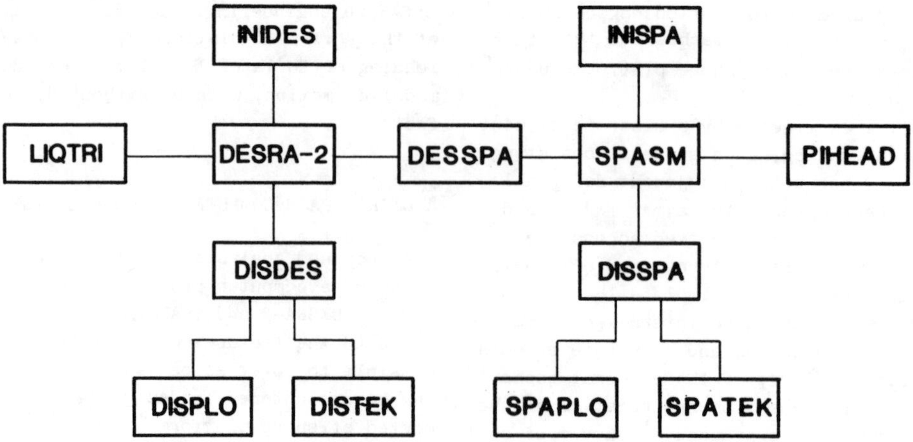

Figure 1. The computer program system

5 CONCLUSION

An analysis procedure for earthquake-resistant design of pile-supported offshore platforms is presented, which involves available approaches for site response and soil-pile interaction analyses.

The most significant geotechnical aspects, such as pore water pressure generation during seismic loading and nonlinear-inelastic characteristics of soil-pile interaction are properly considered.

The analysis is accomplished by coupling two computer programs, namely DESRA-2 and SPASM, which were included in a system of routines for processing I/O data and visualization of results.

The computer program system has been verified, and is presently implemented, on a VAX-11/780 computer and provides a fairly good optimization of the various design phases.

ACKNOWLEDGEMENTS

The work reported herein is part of a research program sponsored by Aquater S.p.A. and carried out with the consultancy of Prof. I.M. Smith, Simon Engineering Laboratories, University of Manchester, and Dr. F. Molenkamp, Delft Geotechnics.

The financial contribution from Delft Geotechnics and the Committee for Applied Scientific Research of Rijkswaterstaat is gratefully acknowledged.

Special thanks are due to Dr. M. Basili and his co-workers, ENEA (Comitato Nazionale per la Ricerca e per lo Sviluppo dell' Energia Nucleare e delle Energie Alternative), Rome, for analysis and processing of strong motion accelerograms.

The computer program system was developped by D. Guanciarossa.

REFERENCES

API (American Petroleum Institute), Recommended Practice for Planning, Designing and Constructing Fixed Offshore Platforms, Seventeenth Edition, Dallas Texas, April 1st, 1987.

Aquater S.p.A., Earthquake-resistant Design of Pile-supported Offshore Platforms. Recommended Approach for the Foundation Performance Analysis and the Evaluation of Input Geotechnical Parameters for the Superstructure Dynamic Analysis, INSU A 1209 Internal Report, November, 1982.

Basili, M. and Brady, G., Low Frequency Filtering and the Selection of Limits for Accelerogram Corrections, Proc. 6th Europ. Conf. on Earthquake Engineering, Dubrovnik, 1978.

Det Norske Veritas, Rules for Design, Construction and Inspection of Offshore Structures, Appendix F, Foundations, and

Appendix G, Dynamic Analysis, Oslo, Norway, 1977.
Finn, W.D.L., Martin, G.R., and Lee, K.W.M. Application of Effective Stress Method for Offshore Seismic Design in Cohesionless Seafloor Soils, Tenth Annual Offshore Technology Conference, Proc., Houston, Texas, May, 1978, Paper No. 3112.
Lee, K.W.M., and Finn, W.D.L., DESRA-2, Dynamic Effective Stress Response Analysis of Soil Deposits with Energy Transmitting Boundary Including Assessment of Liquefaction Potential, Soil Mechanics Series No. 38, Department of Civil Engineering, Univ. of British Columbia, Vancouver, B.C. June, 1978.
Martin, G.R., Finn, W.D.L. and Seed, H.B., Fundamentals of Liquefaction Under Cyclic Loading, Journ. Geotech., Enging. Div., ASCE, Vol. 101, GT5, May, 1975.
Matlock, H. and Foo, S.H.C., Simulation of Lateral Pile Behaviour under Earthquake Motion, a report to Chevron Oil Field Research Company from the Univ. of Texas at Austin, July, 1978.
Matlock, H., Foo, S.H.C., Tsai, C., Lam, I.P.C., SPASM. A Dynamic Beam-Column Program for Seismic Pile Analysis with Support Motion, a documentation report to Chevron Oil Field Research Company from Fugro, Inc., Long Beach, California, August, 1979.
Molenkamp, F. and Di Carlo, A., Liquefaction Parameters of the Seafloor for Earthquake Analysis, Secondo Colloquio di Ingegneria Offshore e Marina, A.I.O.M., Bergamo, Giugno, 1984.
Trifunac, M.D. and Lee, V., Routine Computer Processing of Strong Motion Accelerograms, Earthquake Engineering Laboratory, California Institute of Technology, Pasadena, California, 1973.

APPENDIX

LIQTRI evaluates Finn's liquefaction parameters from undrained cyclic triaxial test results.
INIDES initializes and updates a catalogue of DESRA-2 problem results.
DESRA-2 computes the one-dimensional nonlinear seismic response of soil deposits, with energy transmitting boundary including generation, dissipation and redistribution of pore water pressure.
DISDES processes DESRA-2 output data, produces many kinds of drawings and compares results of different cases studied.
DISPLO, DISTEK produce graphical output of DISDES, respectively on plotter and Tektronix.
DESSPA associates selected soil displacement time-histories to selected pile stations.
INISPA initializes and updates a catalogue of SPASM problem results.
SPASM analyzes soil-pile seismic interaction with a simplified model of the superstructure.
DISSPA processes SPASM output data and graphically reproduces the results;
SPAPLO, SPATEK produce graphical outputs of DISSPA, respectively on plotter and Tektronix.
PIHEAD processes SPASM results for the pilehead station and produces graphical outputs both on plotter and Tektronix.

Numerical Methods in Geomechanics (Innsbruck 1988), Swoboda (ed.)
© 1989 Balkema, Rotterdam. ISBN 90 6191 809 X

Dynamic analysis of effective stress of tailings dams

Zhiying Xu
East China Technical University of Water Resources, Nanjing, People's Republic of China

ABSTRACT: This paper considers the earthquake induced pore water pressure in closed combination with the deformation and consolidation of tailings (earth) dam and foundation, thus introducing the earthquake pore water pressure into the Biot's equation, which is then solved by FEM to obtain displacements and residual pore water pressure. This would constitute a reasonable method of dynamic analysis of tailings (earth) dams. The FEM is based on the Galerkin's weighted residual method. Finally a numerical result is given for a tailings dam.

1. INTRODUCTION

In recent years great efforts have been made to investigate the liquefaction of tailings sands under earthquake motion, the dynamic testing technique of tailings (soils) and analytical procedure is also being improved (see Seed et al. (1975) and Xu Zhiying and Shen Zhujiang (1981)).Particularly, the application of FEM in dynamic analysis of tailings and soils offers a useful means for resolving many complicated engineering problems in connection with tailings liquefaction. But the conventional methods of dynamic analysis are based on the total stress principle, and they do not take into account the degradation of soil (tailings) due to the rise of pore pressure, to say nothing of its dissipation and redistribution(see Mejia and Seed (1987)).Generally speaking, the generation of pore water pressure is always accompanied with its diffusion and dissipation. Some investigation have been made to study this coupled effect, but most published methods are based on the Terzaghi's consolidation theory. With regard to the deformation and consolidation of tailings and soil as a unified process, the Biot's theory is undoubtely more rigorous than Terzaghi's theory. The limitation of the use of Biot's theory is believed to be due to the mathematical difficulties. In the following we shall introduce the increase of pore water pressure induced by earthquake into the Biot's equations, and solve them by FEM to determine the time-dependent distribution of pore water pressure. The non-linear dynamic analysis is carried out based on effective stress principle in coupling with pore water pressure change.

2. THEORY AND BASIC EQUATIONS

2.1 Equilibrim equations

If we consider the tailings as a linearly elastic porous medium and introduce the generated rise of pore water pressure into the equilibrium equations, we get

$$\frac{\partial \sigma_x'}{\partial x} + \frac{\partial \tau_{xy}}{\partial y} + \frac{\partial p}{\partial x} - X = 0 \qquad (1)$$

$$\frac{\partial \tau_{xy}}{\partial x} + \frac{\partial \sigma_y'}{\partial y} + \frac{\partial p}{\partial y} - Y = 0 \qquad (2)$$

where p is residul pore water pressure (including the seismic-induced pore water pressure p_g), σ_x' and σ_y' are components of effective stress tensor, x, y are coordinates in horizontal and vertical directions, and X, Y are body forces of tailings (soil) element.

2.2 Geometric equations

Taking compressive strain as positive, the geometric equations of deformation are as follows

$$\varepsilon_x = -\frac{\partial u}{\partial x}, \quad \varepsilon_y = -\frac{\partial v}{\partial y}, \quad \gamma_{xy} = -\frac{\partial u}{\partial y} - \frac{\partial v}{\partial x} \quad (3)$$

where $\varepsilon_x, \varepsilon_y, \gamma_{xy}$ are components of strain tensor, u, v are displacements of soil skeleton in x and y directions

2.3 Hooke's law

$$\left.\begin{aligned} \sigma_x' &= E_1\,\varepsilon_x + E_2\,\varepsilon_y - p_g \\ \sigma_y' &= E_2\,\varepsilon_x + E_1\,\varepsilon_y - p_g \\ \tau_{xy} &= E_3\,\gamma_{xy} \end{aligned}\right\} \quad (4)$$

where p_g is seismic pore water pressure and

$$E_1 = \frac{E(1-\mu)}{(1+\mu)(1-2\mu)}, \quad E_2 = \frac{E\mu}{(1+\mu)(1-2\mu)}$$

$$E_3 = \frac{E}{2(1+\mu)}$$

with E and μ being Young's modulus and Poisson's ratio.

2.4 Darcy's law

$$\left.\begin{aligned} q_x &= -\bar{k}_x\frac{\partial p}{\partial x} = -\frac{k_x}{\gamma_w}\frac{\partial p}{\partial x} \\ q_y &= -\bar{k}_y\frac{\partial p}{\partial y} = -\frac{k_y}{\gamma_w}\frac{\partial p}{\partial y} \end{aligned}\right\} \quad (5)$$

where k_x, k_y are coefficients of permeability in x and y directions, γ_w is unite weight of water, q_x, q_y are seepage velocity in x and y directions.

2.5 Continuity condition of water flow

$$\frac{\partial q_x}{\partial x} + \frac{\partial q_y}{\partial y} = \frac{\partial}{\partial t}(\varepsilon_x + \varepsilon_y) \quad (6)$$

where t is time.

2.6 Governing differential equations

Substituting eq.(3) into eq.(4) and then into eq.(1) and (2), we get two equations containing 3 unknowns u, v and p as follows

$$E_1\frac{\partial^2 u}{\partial x^2} + E_3\frac{\partial^2 u}{\partial y^2} + (E_2 + E_3)\frac{\partial^2 v}{\partial x \partial y} - \frac{\partial p}{\partial x} + \frac{\partial p_g}{\partial x} + X = 0 \quad (7)$$

$$E_3\frac{\partial^2 v}{\partial x^2} + E_1\frac{\partial^2 v}{\partial y^2} + (E_2 + E_3)\frac{\partial^2 u}{\partial x \partial y} - \frac{\partial p}{\partial y} + \frac{\partial p_g}{\partial y} + Y = 0 \quad (8)$$

One more equation may be derived by substituting eq.(3) and (5) into eq.(6)

$$\bar{k}_x\frac{\partial^2 p}{\partial x^2} + \bar{k}_y\frac{\partial^2 p}{\partial y^2} = \frac{\partial}{\partial t}\left(\frac{\partial u}{\partial x} + \frac{\partial v}{\partial y}\right) \quad (9)$$

Equations (7), (8) and (9) constitute the governing equations of Biot's consolidation theory, which can be solved numerically under giving boundary and initial conditions.

2.7 Formula of seismic pore water pressure

Based upon the experimental data of tailings sands, we get the following formula for predicting the seismic pore water pressure:

$$\Delta p_g \; \frac{\sigma_{mo}'(1-mS_L)}{\pi\theta N_L\sqrt{1-\left(\frac{N}{N_L}\right)^{1/\theta}}}\left(\frac{N}{N_L}\right)^{\frac{1}{2\theta}-1}\Delta N \quad (10)$$

where Δp_g is increment of pore water pressure in ΔN loading cycles, σ_{mo}' is mean initial effective stress, N_L is number of cycles to cause liquefaction, N is number of loading cycles (seismic equivalent number N_{eq}), S_L is static stress level, m and θ are constants.

2.8 Formula of seismic residual deformation

The formula of seismic residual deformation determined by cyclic triaxial test is

$$\Delta\gamma_s = C_1(S_L)^{n_1}\left(\frac{\tau_d}{\sigma_{mo}}\right)^{n_2}\frac{\Delta N}{1+N} \quad (11)$$

where $\Delta\gamma_s$ is increment of residual shape deformation in N loading cycles, τ_d is dynamic shear stress in 45°plane, C_1, n_1, n_2 are tailings constants, others have the same meaning as before.

3. FINITE ELEMENT FORMULATION

We shall solved the basic euqtions (7), (8), (9) numerically using FEM. Firstly the unknown variables u, v and p are represented by the following approximate functions

$$\left.\begin{aligned} u &= \sum_{i=1}^{n} N_i(x,y)\,u_i(t) \\ v &= \sum_{i=1}^{n} N_i(x,y)\,v_i(t) \\ p &= \sum_{i=1}^{n} N_i(x,y)\,p_i(t) \end{aligned}\right\} \quad (12)$$

in which N_i is piece-wise continious function in x-y plane, or so-called shape function, it takes value 1 in node i and vanishes in other nodes, u_i, v_i and p_i are unknown time-dependent node value, n is number of all nodes.

In formulating finite element equations the weighted residual method will be used. If we take the shape function as a weighted function as proposed by Galerkin (see Zienkiewicz (1971)), we can get the following 3n equations from basic equation (7), (8) and (9)

$$\iint_A N_i\left[\left(E_1\frac{\partial^2}{\partial x^2}+E_3\frac{\partial^2}{\partial y^2}\right)u+(E_2+E_3)\frac{\partial^2}{\partial x\partial y}v-\frac{\partial}{\partial x}p+\frac{\partial}{\partial x}p_g+X\right]dx\,dy=0 \tag{13}$$

$$\iint_A N_i\left[(E_3+E_2)\frac{\partial^2}{\partial x\partial y}u+\left(E_3\frac{\partial^2}{\partial x^2}+E_1\frac{\partial^2}{\partial y^2}\right)v-\frac{\partial}{\partial y}p+\frac{\partial}{\partial y}p_g+Y\right]dx\,dy=0 \tag{14}$$

$$\iint_A N_i\left[-\frac{\partial}{\partial x}\frac{\partial u}{\partial t}-\frac{\partial}{\partial y}\frac{\partial v}{\partial t}+\left(\bar{k}_x\frac{\partial^2}{\partial x^2}+\bar{k}_y\frac{\partial^2}{\partial y^2}\right)p\right]dx\,dy=0 \tag{15}$$

A is the area of interested region, i= 1, 2, 3,......n. By using partial integration technique the equations (13), (14) and (15) can be transformed as follows

$$\iint_A\left[\left(E_1\frac{\partial N_i}{\partial x}\frac{\partial}{\partial x}+E_3\frac{\partial N_i}{\partial y}\frac{\partial}{\partial y}\right)u+\left(E_2\frac{\partial N_i}{\partial x}\frac{\partial}{\partial y}+E_3\frac{\partial N_i}{\partial y}\frac{\partial}{\partial x}\right)v-\frac{\partial N_i}{\partial x}p\right]dx\,dy$$
$$=\iint_A\left(N_iX-\frac{\partial N_i}{\partial x}p_g\right)dx\,dy+\oint_s N_i\left[\left(E_1\frac{\partial}{\partial x}l_x+E_3\frac{\partial}{\partial y}l_y\right)u+\left(E_2\frac{\partial}{\partial y}l_x+E_3\frac{\partial}{\partial x}l_y\right)v-pl_x+p_g l_x\right]ds \tag{16}$$

$$\iint_A\left[\left(E_3\frac{\partial N_i}{\partial x}\frac{\partial}{\partial y}+E_2\frac{\partial N_i}{\partial y}\frac{\partial}{\partial x}\right)u+\left(E_3\frac{\partial N_i}{\partial x}\frac{\partial}{\partial x}+E_1\frac{\partial N_i}{\partial y}\frac{\partial}{\partial y}\right)v-\frac{\partial N_i}{\partial y}p\right]dx\,dy$$
$$=\iint_A\left(N_iY-\frac{\partial N_i}{\partial y}p_g\right)dx\,dy+\oint_s N_i\left[\left(E_2\frac{\partial}{\partial x}l_y+E_3\frac{\partial}{\partial y}l_x\right)u+\left(E_3\frac{\partial}{\partial x}l_x+E_1\frac{\partial}{\partial y}l_y\right)v-pl_y+p_g l_y\right]ds \tag{17}$$

$$\iint_A\left[-N_i\frac{\partial}{\partial x}\frac{\partial u}{\partial t}-N_i\frac{\partial}{\partial y}\frac{\partial v}{\partial t}-\left(\bar{k}_x\frac{\partial N_i}{\partial x}\frac{\partial}{\partial x}+\bar{k}_y\frac{\partial N_i}{\partial y}\frac{\partial}{\partial y}\right)p\right]dx\,dy=-\oint_S N_i\left(\bar{k}_x\frac{\partial}{\partial x}l_x+\bar{k}_y\frac{\partial}{\partial y}l_y\right)p\,ds \tag{18}$$

Substituting the approximate function (12) of u, v, p into these relations, and then considering the equations (3) and (4) leds to

$$\sum_{j=1}^{n}\left[k_{ij}^{11}u_j(t)+k_{ij}^{12}v_j(t)+k_{ij}^{13}p_j(t)\right]=F_i^1(t) \tag{19}$$

$$\sum_{j=1}^{n}\left[k_{ij}^{21}u_j(t)+k_{ij}^{22}v_j(t)+k_{ij}^{23}p_j(t)\right]=F_i^2(t) \tag{20}$$

$$\sum_{j=1}^{n}\left[k_{ij}^{31}\frac{du_j(t)}{dt}+k_{ij}^{32}\frac{dv_j(t)}{dt}+2k_{ij}^{33}p_j(t)\right]=F_i^3(t)$$

$$i=1,2,3\cdots\cdots n \tag{21}$$

With

$$\left.\begin{aligned}
k_{ij}^{11}&=\iint_A\left(E_1\frac{\partial N_i}{\partial x}\frac{\partial N_j}{\partial x}+E_3\frac{\partial N_i}{\partial y}\frac{\partial N_j}{\partial y}\right)dx\,dy\\
k_{ij}^{22}&=\iint_A\left(E_3\frac{\partial N_i}{\partial x}\frac{\partial N_j}{\partial x}+E_1\frac{\partial N_i}{\partial y}\frac{\partial N_j}{\partial y}\right)dx\,dy\\
k_{ij}^{33}&=-\frac{1}{2}\iint_A\left(\bar{k}_x\frac{\partial N_i}{\partial x}\frac{\partial N_j}{\partial x}+\bar{k}_y\frac{\partial N_i}{\partial y}\frac{\partial N_j}{\partial y}\right)dx\,dy\\
k_{ij}^{12}&=\iint_A\left(E_2\frac{\partial N_i}{\partial x}\frac{\partial N_j}{\partial y}+E_3\frac{\partial N_i}{\partial y}\frac{\partial N_j}{\partial x}\right)dx\,dy\\
k_{ij}^{21}&=\iint_A\left(E_3\frac{\partial N_i}{\partial x}\frac{\partial N_j}{\partial y}+E_2\frac{\partial N_i}{\partial y}\frac{\partial N_j}{\partial x}\right)dx\,dy\\
k_{ij}^{13}&=-\iint_A N_j\frac{\partial N_i}{\partial x}dx\,dy\\
k_{ij}^{31}&=-\iint_A N_i\frac{\partial N_j}{\partial x}dx\,dy\\
k_{ij}^{23}&=-\iint_A N_j\frac{\partial N_i}{\partial y}dx\,dy\\
k_{ij}^{32}&=-\iint_A N_i\frac{\partial N_j}{\partial y}dx\,dy\\
F_i^1(t)&=\iint_A\left(N_iX-\frac{\partial N_i}{\partial x}p_g\right)dx\,dy-\oint_s N_i f_x\,ds\\
F_i^2(t)&=\iint_A\left(N_iY-\frac{\partial N_i}{\partial y}p_g\right)dx\,dy-\oint_s N_i f_y\,ds\\
F_i^3(t)&=\oint_S N_i q_n\,ds
\end{aligned}\right\} \tag{22}$$

where $f_x=\sigma_x' l_x+\tau_{xy}l_y+pl_x$, $f_y=\sigma_y' l_y+\tau_{xy}l_x+pl_y$ are prescribed boundary loading, $q_n=q_x l_x+q_y l_y$ is prescribed boundary infiltration, l_x, l_y are the direction cosine of the outward normal and the x, y direction, and integral s is taken over the whole boundary.

By differentiating eq.(19) and (20) with respect to time t, a complete set of 3n ordinary differential equations is obtained, and to solve them the central finite difference technique will be used. Let Δu_i, Δv_i and Δp_i be the increments of node variable u_i , v_i and p_i in node i, in time increment Δt, u_{io}, v_{io} and p_{io} be the initial value of these variables at the beginning of this time increment, $p_{io}+\Delta p_i/2$ be the mean value of p_i , the following set of finite difference equations is obtained from eq. (19), (20) and (21).

$$\sum_{j=1}^{n}\left[k_{ij}^{11}\Delta u_j + k_{ij}^{12}\Delta v_j + k_{ij}^{13}\Delta p_j\right] = \Delta F_i^1 \qquad (23)$$

$$\sum_{j=1}^{n}\left[k_{ij}^{21}\Delta u_j + k_{ij}^{22}\Delta v_j + k_{ij}^{23}\Delta p_j\right] = \Delta F_i^2 \qquad (24)$$

$$\sum_{j=1}^{n}\left[k_{ij}^{31}\Delta u_j + k^{32}\Delta v_j + k_{ij}^{33}\Delta p_j\right] = \overline{\Delta F_i^3} \qquad (25)$$

Since the body force X and Y do not change with time, only the loading increment, the increment of seismic pore pressure and the increment of infiltration give contribution to the right hand terms in the eq.(23), (24) and (25), i.e.

$$\Delta F_i^1(t) = -\iint_A \frac{\partial N_i}{\partial x}\Delta p_g\,dx\,dy - \oint_S N_i\,\Delta f_x\,ds \qquad (26)$$

$$\Delta F_i^2(t) = -\iint_A \frac{\partial N_i}{\partial y}\Delta p_g\,dx\,dy - \oint_S N_i\,\Delta f_y\,ds \qquad (27)$$

$$\overline{\Delta F_i^3}(t) = \oint_S N_i\,\Delta q_n\,ds - 2\Delta t\sum_{j=1}^{n} k_{ij}^{33}\,p_{jo} \qquad (28)$$

In which $\Delta f_x, \Delta f_y$ and Δq_n are prescribed boundary conditions, Δp_g is the increment of seismic pore pressure in time increment Δt, computed from eq.(10).

Equation system (23), (24) and (25) contains 3n algebraic equations with 3n unknowns Δu , Δv and Δp (i=1.........n), and may be solved by matrix triangulation technique.

4. ANALYTICAL PROCEDURES

In this paper the effective stress method for dynamic analysis will be adopted. In order to incorporated the generation, diffusion and dissipation of pore water pressure into the dynamic analysis, the whole period of earthquake motion is subdivided into several time steps. For each time step the non-linear dynamic response analysis is carried out, the dynamic stress is calculated, and the increment of generated pore water pressure Δp_g and residual deformation $\Delta\gamma_s$ in individual element are evaluated. These Δp_g and $\Delta\gamma_s$ are converted into equavalent node force to the loading terms of eq. (26) and (27). Then the resulting simultanious equations are solved to find the increments of displacements and pore pressure, from which a static effective stress field is obtained. New values of modulus are compatible with these new effective stresses. In addition, since the modulus and damping are also strain dependent, several iterations are needed in the dynamic analysis for each time step, for the first iteration values are assigned as those in the last time step. The procedure is carried out step by step until the end of earthquake motion. Several time steps are also needed for post-earthquake static analysis to search the pore water pressure dissipation. In the following some details are given for various stages of calculation.

4.1 Pre-earthquake static analysis

For static analysis Duncan's (1970) non-linear elastic model for tailings is used.

4.2 Equivalent visco-elastic solid

Assuming tailings as equivalent visco-elastic solid, we use the empirical relationships proposed by Hardin and Drnevich (1972) for shear modulus G and damping ratio D.

4.3 Integration of equation of motion

Direct integration method is used to solve following equation of motion

$$[M]\{\ddot{\delta}\} + [C]\{\dot{\delta}\} + [K]\{\delta\} = \{F(t)\} \qquad (29)$$

in which [M] , [K] and [C] are mass, stiffness and damping matrix respectively, $\{F(t)\}$ = nodal earthquake load vector, and δ , $\dot{\delta}$, $\ddot{\delta}$ are nodal displacement, velocity and accerelation vetor relative to bedrock motion.

4.4 Number of loading cycles to cause liquefaction

Following empirical formula is used to estimate the number of cycles to cause liquefaction for each element

$$N_L = 10^{\frac{b - \tau_d/\sigma'_{mo}}{a}} \qquad (30)$$

in which $\tau_d = \tau_{av} = 0.65\tau'_{max}$, τ_{av} is the average shear stress amplitude with τ'_{max} as the maximum value in this time step, σ'_{mo} is mean initial effective stress, and a and b are tailings constant.

4.5 Equivalent number of loading cycles

In this paper simplified method originally proposed by Martin and Seed(1979) is used to estimate the equivalent number of loading cycles.

4.6 Pore water pressure increment and residual deformation increment

Seismic pore water pressure increment Δp_g and residual deformation $\Delta \gamma_s$ are calculated by eq.(10) and eq.(11) respectively, and then they are inverted to the equivalent nodal force F_g.

4.7 Static analysis

After substituting F_g into eq.(23) and (24), the set of eq.(23), (24) and (25) is solved to give the nodal displacements and residual pore water pressure.

4.8 Stress computation

Strain and stress fields are computed from nodal displacement, and on substituting new value of mean effective stress σ_m' into Hardin's (1972) formula, new value of modulus G is obtained for each element and is used for first iteration of the next time step calculation.

4.9 Steps 4.3-4.8 are repeated until the end of earthquake motion. Post-earthquake static analysis are continued until no dissipation of water pressure is revealed.

5. COMPUTED EXAMPLES

The suggested procedure of analysis has been used for several tailings dams. As an example, one of them is given below.

The tailings dam of Maanshan Iron Mine is located in the south of Anhui Province, about 50 km south of Maanshan city. The dam section is shown in Fig.1. The slope of outer surface is 1:5, maximum dam height is 135m. The dam material consists of tailings fine sand, medium sand and slime, and is built on bedrock. The tailings sand has a uniform gradation and large void ratio. It is very liable to liquely under vibration. The

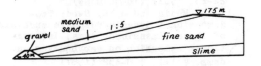

Fig.1 Section of Maanshan tailings dam

dam is located in an earthquake area with intensity VII of modified Mercalli scale. It is necessary to investigate the anti-liquefaction stability of this dam under earthquake motion.

In computation an accelerogram of Songpan earthquake (Aug. 15, 1976, in Sichuan Province) is used as the input bedrock motion with the peak acceleration being scaled to 0.1g and the predominant period being prolonged to 0.24 second. The duration of motion is 10 seconds (Fig.2).

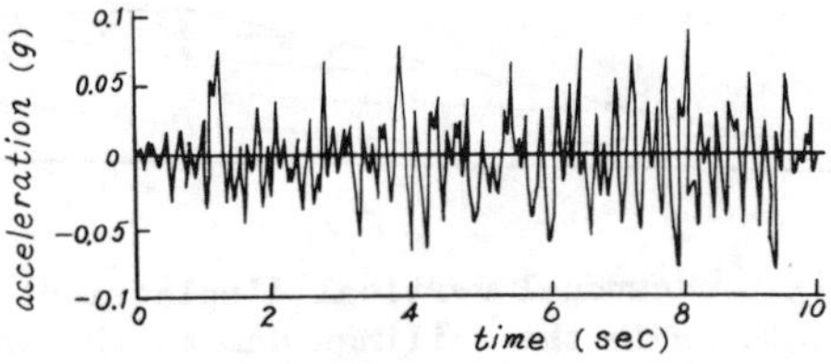

Fig.2 Accelerogram of Songpan earthquake

Figure 3 and figure 4 show residual pore water pressure contours in the dam at end of earthquake motion and at t= 4 days after earthquake respectively. Figure 5 expresses the liquefied region (shaded area) at the end of earthquake. Figure 6 and figure 7 show distribution of residual vertical displacement in the dam at the end of earthquake and at t=4 days of earthquake motion respectively.

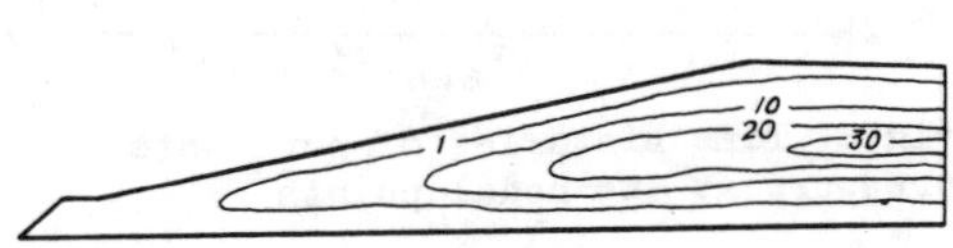

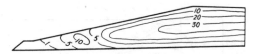

Fig.3 Residual pore water pressure contours at end of earthquake (values are in kP_a)

Fig.4 Residual pore water pressure contours at t=4 days after earthquake (values are in kP_a)

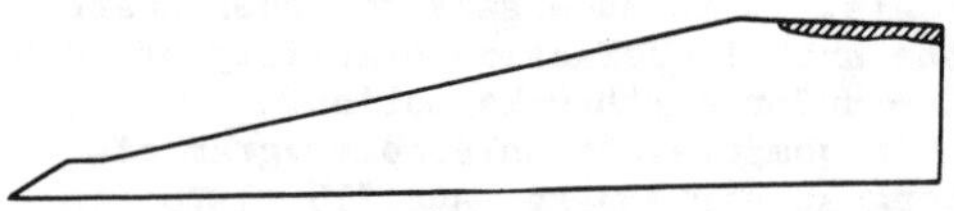

Fig.5 Liquefied region in tailings dam at the end of earthquake motion

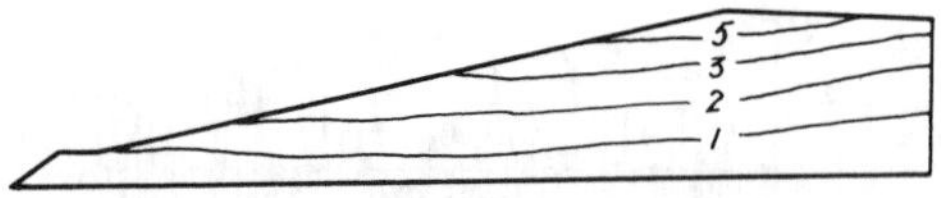

Fig.6 Resudual vertical displacement contours in the tailings dam at the end of earthquake (values are in cm)

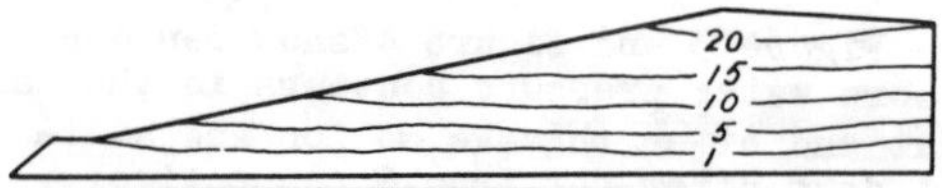

Fig.7 Resudual vertical displacement contours in the tailings dam at t=4 days of earthquake (value are in cm)

Figure 8 shows the time histories of pore water pressure in two typical nodal points. It can be seen that the dissipation of pore water pressure is very slow.

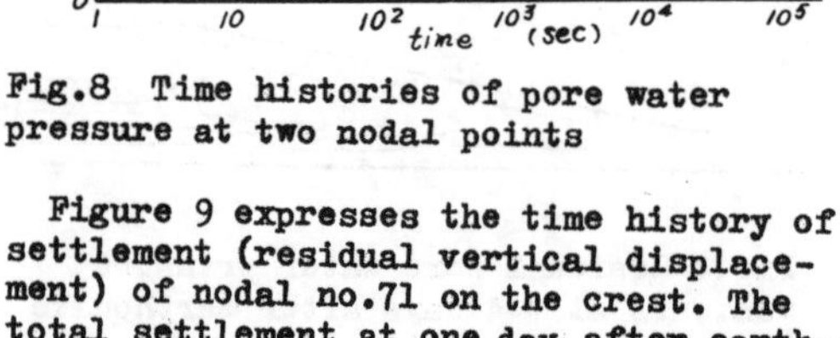

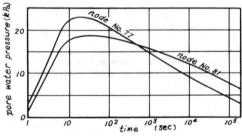

Fig.8 Time histories of pore water pressure at two nodal points

Figure 9 expresses the time history of settlement (residual vertical displacement) of nodal no.71 on the crest. The total settlement at one day after earthquake approaches 16 cm, the probable final settlement is evaluated to be about 25 cm.

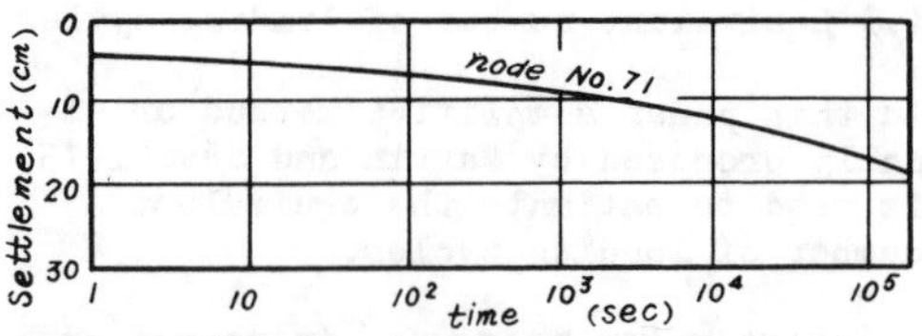

Fig.9 Time history of settlement of nodal no.71 on the crest

6. CONCLUSION

A procedure of dynamic analysis of effective stress for the evaluation of the seismic response of tailings (earth) dams has been presented in this paper. By its application not only the response time histories of stress, strain and acceleration can be determined, but also the generation, diffusion and dissipation of pore pressure and permanent deformation can be estimated in the saturated tailings during the course of earthquake motion and post-earthquake.

A dynamic analysis of effective stress of Maanshan tailings dam has shown that residual pore water pressure of different magnitudes in the dam may happen, especially near the dam axis, under an earthquake with intensity XII of modified Mercalli scale. Owing to the high water pressure there may be a thickness of about 5 m of liquefied zone within a restricted region near the crest, at the end of earthquake motion. It is possible that a local and limited sliding due to residual pore water pressure may occur.

REFERENCES

[1] H. B. Seed, K. L. Lee, I. M. Idriss and Makdisi: The slides in the Lower San Fernando Dams during the earthquake of February 9, 1971, Proc. ASCE, Vol.101, No.GT7, 651-688 (1975)

[2] Xu Zhiying and Shen Zhujiang: Liquefaction and stability analysis of a high tailing dam under earthquake excitation, Chinese Journal of Geotechnical Engineering, Vol.3, No.4, 22-23 (1981) (in Chinese)

[3] L. H. Mejia and H. B. Seed: Two-dimensional dynamic response analysis of three-dimensional dams, International symposium on earthquakes and dams, Vol.1. 418-432 (1987)

[4] O. C. Zienkiewicz, The finite element method in engineering science, McGraw, Londan, 1971

Numerical Methods in Geomechanics (Innsbruck 1988), Swoboda (ed.)
© 1989 Balkema, Rotterdam. ISBN 90 6191 809 X

Back analysis of measured rheologic displacement of underground openings

Zhiyin Wang & Huaiheng Liu
Xi' an Mining Institute, Xi' an, People' s Republic of China

ABSTRACT Based on the finite element equations, a back analysis method (BAM) is presented by in-situ time-dependent displacements. The method can be used in evaluating the initial stress in ground, elastic modulus and viscoelastic parameters of rock mass. In this paper, we have worked out the calculating formulas which considered both the rheologic properties of rock mass and the spatial effect of working face. A finite element method (FEM) computer program was completed with the function of back analysis (BA). Finally some calculating examples showed that the method is correct and practical.

INTRODUCTION

The monitoring technique and the BAM of displacement measurement have aroused engineer's interest in underground engineering, and some researchers have published a lot of papers on this problem. However, the most of papers is based on the assumption of linear elasticity. It is well known that, the displacement of surrounding rock usually develops with time after excavation of underground caverns, and lasts a long time. The linear elastic analysis not only producers the large calculating error, but also can not predicts the development of deformation. Therefore the solution from it does not play a role in guiding practice. In this paper we gave a new BAM and its formulas via considering the time dependence and combining FEM with the regression analysis or optimization method. Some examples of engineerings are given out.

FUNDAMENTAL FORMULAS OF RHEOLOGIC BA

The following assumptions are adopted in the paper :

1. The rock mass is homogeneous and isotropic.
2. The initial stress field in ground is homogeneous; that is

$$\{\sigma_o\} = \{\sigma_{xo} \quad \sigma_{yo} \quad \tau_{xyo}\}^T$$

where the vertical component σ_{yo} is a function of the depth H and the unit weight γ of the ground media, so we have

$$\sigma_{yo} = \gamma H$$

3. The external load does not vary between two steps of excavation.

Now, the general constitutive equation under the viscoelastic state can be written

$$\{\varepsilon^v\} = \frac{1}{E(t)}[C_o]\{\sigma_t\} \qquad (1)$$

Where $[C_o]$ is Poisson's ratio matrix For a plane strain case it is

$$[C_o] = \begin{bmatrix} 1-\mu^2 & -\mu(1+\mu) & 0 \\ -\mu(1+\mu) & 1-\mu^2 & 0 \\ 0 & 0 & 2(1+\mu) \end{bmatrix} \qquad (2)$$

$\{\sigma_t\}$ is the stress vector at the t time, $\{\varepsilon^v\}$ is the creep strain vector, E(t) is viscoelastic modulus depending on the rheologic model. For some useful viscoelastic models the expressions of E(t) are listed in Table 1.
At the t moment the total strain $\{\varepsilon_t\}$ at any point is

$$\{\varepsilon_t\} = \{\varepsilon_e\} + \{\varepsilon^v\} \qquad (3)$$

and the relationship between stress and strain is

$$\{\sigma_t\} = [D](\{\varepsilon_t\} - \{\varepsilon^v\}) \quad (4)$$

where $[D] = E_o\,[C_o]^{-1}$, is elastic matrix, E_o is Young's modulus, $\{\varepsilon_e\}$ is elastic strain vector.

The FEM equilibrium equation at any moment is

$$\Sigma\int_{\Omega}[B]^T\,\{\sigma_t\}\,d\Omega - \{P^n\} = 0 \quad (5)$$

Where $\{P^n\}$ is the load vector at t_n the time, and $[B]$ is the geometric matrix of element. From equation (1),(4) and (5) we can obtain

$$[K^*]\,\{u(t)\} = \{P^n\}\,/E_v(t) \quad (6)$$

$[K^*]$ is unit general stiffness matrix, and $[K^*] = (1/E_o)\,[K]$, $E_v(t)$ is composite modulus and may be written

$$E_v(t) = E_oE(t)/(E_o + E(t)) \quad (7)$$

For some useful viscoelastic models $E_v(t)$ may be also seen in Table 1.

If the other construction steps are not operated after excavation, $\{P^n\}$ is still the equivalent nodal force on the surface of excavation. It can be written

$$\{P^n\} = \{P_o\} = [P^*]\cdot\{\sigma_o\} \quad (8)$$

where $[P^*] = [P_x \;\; P_y \;\; P_{xy}]$

P_x, P_y, P_{xy} are the vectors of the equivalent nodal force formed by unit σ_{xo}, σ_{yo}, τ_{xyo}, respectively.

So the formula (6) may be rewritten as

$$[K^*]\,\{u(t)\} = [P^*]\{\sigma_o\}/\,E_v(t) \quad (9)$$

or

$$\{u(t)\} = [A]\,\{\bar{\sigma}_o\} \quad (10)$$

where

$$\{\bar{\sigma}_o\} = \{\sigma_{xo}/E_v(t) \quad \sigma_{yo}/E_v(t) \quad \tau_{xyo}/E_v(t)\}^T \quad (11)$$

$$[A] = [K^*]^{-1}[P^*] \quad (12)$$

If the displacement vector at the measuring points in $\{u_1(t)\}$, then equation (10) relative to $\{u_1(t)\}$ can be changed as follows [1]

$$\{u_1(t)\} = [A_1]\,\{\bar{\sigma}_o\} \quad (13)$$

When the measured displacements are relative values, $\{u_1(t)\}$ in equation(13) should be transformed into the relative displacement $\{\Delta u(t)\}$, and the equation (13) is changed into

$$\{\Delta u(t)\} = [A^*]\,\{\bar{\sigma}_o\} \quad (14)$$

where [1]

$$[A^*] = [T]\,[A_1]$$

$$[T] = \begin{bmatrix} -\cos\theta & -\sin\theta & \cos\theta & \sin\theta \\ \sin\theta & -\cos\theta & -\sin\theta & \cos\theta \end{bmatrix}$$

The least square solution of formula (14) is :

$$\{\bar{\sigma}_o\} = (\,[A^*]^T\,[A^*]\,)^{-1}\cdot[A^*]^T\{\Delta u(t)\} \quad (15)$$

It should be noticed that the displacement measurement is often conducted after excavation in practice, so a part of displacement has taken place before setting up the measuring points, and its influence on the back analysis results can not be ignored. Therefore, we make the following modification for the above equations :

1. Only considering rheologic factor

According to formulas (13) and (11), the displacement vector at t=ti can be derived as follows :

$$\{u_1(t_i)\} = \frac{E_o\,\{u_1(o)\}}{E_v(t_i)} \quad (16)$$

If the measuring points are installed at $t=t_o$ after excavation, from equation (16) we may obtain the displacement at to :

$$\{u_1(t_o)\} = \frac{E_o\{u_1(o)\}}{E_v(t_o)} \quad (17)$$

Since the real displacement $\{u_1(t)\}$ is equal to the sum of the measured value $\{\tilde{u}(t_i)\}$ and the displacement $\{u_1(t_o)\}$ before setting up measuring points. From formulas (16), (17), (13) and (11), we could get

$$\{\tilde{u}(t_i)\} = \frac{[A_1]\{\sigma_o\}}{E'(t_i)} \quad (18)$$

Corresponding to measuring relative displacement $\{\Delta\tilde{u}(t_i)\}$, equation (18) can be rewritten

$$\{\Delta\tilde{u}(t_i)\} = \frac{[A^*]\{\sigma_o\}}{E'(t_i)} \quad (19)$$

Then relying on formula (15), we have

$$\{\sigma_o\}/E'(t_i) = ([A^*]^T[A^*])^{-1} \cdot [A^*]^T\{\Delta\tilde{u}(t_i)\} \quad (20)$$

where

$$1/E'(t_i) = 1/E_v(t_i) - 1/E_v(t_o) \quad (21)$$

2. Considering spatial effect and rheologic factor

Generally, the measuring points in tunnel are set up as nearly to the working face as possible, and the first measurement is immediately carried out. In this case, the spatial effect of working face has an influence on measured results. We assume that the time of 1st, 2nd, ..., jth advance of working face after setting up measuring points is respectively, t_1, t_2, ..., t_j, the corresponding load release coefficient is α_1, α_2, ..., α_j, the instantaneous load release coefficient is α_o, and the time setting up the measuring points is t_o ($0 < t_o < t_1$). Therefore, when $0 < t_i < t_1$, the real displacement is equal to the displacement caused by the equivalent release load $\alpha_o\{P_o\}$, i.e. by formula (16).

$$\{u_1(t_i)\} = (\{u_1(o)\} \cdot E_o/E_v(t_i))\,\alpha_o$$

The displacement before setting up measuring points is

$$\{u_1(t_o)\} = \alpha_o\{u_1(o)\}\,E_o/E_v(t_o) \quad (22)$$

The real displacement at t_i ($t_1 < t_i < t_2$) includes two parts that one is caused by $\alpha_o\{P_o\}$ and the other by the equivalent release load $(\alpha_1 - \alpha_o)\{P_o\}$ of the advance of working face at the t_1 time. So we get

$$\{u_1(t_i)\} = \left[\frac{\alpha_o}{E_v(t_i)} + \frac{\alpha_1 - \alpha_o}{E_v(t_i - t_1)}\right] \cdot E_o\{u_1(o)\} \quad (23)$$

The measured displacement is the difference between $\{u_1(t_i)\}$ and $\{u_1(t_o)\}$, i.e.

$$\{\tilde{u}(t_i)\} = \left[\left(\frac{1}{E_v(t_1)} - \frac{1}{E_v(t_o)}\right) + \frac{\alpha_1 - \alpha_o}{E_v(t_i - t_1)}\right] \cdot E_o\{u_1(o)\}$$

or $\{\tilde{u}(t_i)\} = [A_1]\{\sigma_o\}/E'(t_i, \alpha_1)$

Similarly, when $t_i > t_j$, we have

$$\{\tilde{u}(t_i)\} = [A_1]\{\sigma_o\}/E'(t_i, \alpha_j) \quad (24)$$

where

$$\frac{1}{E'(t_i\ \alpha_j)} = \alpha_o\left(\frac{1}{E_v(t_i)} - \frac{1}{E_v(t_o)}\right) + \sum_{m=1}^{j}\left(\frac{\alpha_m - \alpha_{m-1}}{E_v(t_i - t_m)}\right) \quad (25)$$

α_m (m=1, j) may be determined by measuring results or incremental back analysis considering spatial effect. So the solution of formula (24) to the relative measuring value $\{\Delta\tilde{u}(t_i)\}$

$$\{\sigma_o\}/E'(t_i, \alpha_j) = ([A^*]^T[A^*])^{-1} \cdot [A^*]^T\{\Delta\tilde{u}(t_i)\} \quad (26)$$

The initial stress (σ_o) in ground and

$E'(t_i)$ or $E'(t_i, \alpha_j)$ are obtained using formula (20) or (26) by the measuring value $\{\Delta\tilde{u}(t_i)\}$ of all measuring points at the t_i time. For different time $t_i (i=1,n)$ we can obtain a group values of $E'(t_i)$ or $E'(t_i, \alpha_j)$.

REGRESSION ANALYSIS AND OPTIMIZATION METHOD OF VISCOELASTIC PARAMETERS

That $E'(t_i)$ or $E'(t_i, \alpha_j)$ (i=1,2,... ...n) is the function of viscoelastic parameters, thus the viscoelastic parameters can be back calculated from it by use of the regression analysis or the optimization method.

If the observation is made for a long time we, let $t \to \infty$, can obtain $E'(\infty)$. Substituting it into formula (21), the following equation is gotten

$$\frac{1}{E'(\infty)} - \frac{1}{E'(t_i)} = \frac{1}{E_v(\infty)} - \frac{1}{E_v(t_i)} \tag{27}$$

By a similar way we can derive following formula considering spatial effect from eq.(25)

$$\frac{1}{E'(\infty,\alpha_j)} - \frac{1}{E'(t_i,\alpha_j)} = \alpha_0 \left(\frac{1}{E_v(\infty)} - \frac{1}{E_v(t_i)} + \sum_{m+1}^{j}(\alpha_m - \alpha_{m-1})\left(\frac{1}{E_v(\infty)} - \frac{1}{E_v(t_i-t_m)}\right)\right) \tag{28}$$

The composite modulus Ev(t) used rheologic model is substituted into Eq. (27) and Eq.(28) and then the regression analysis is carried out through linearization to obtain the elastic modulus and rheologic parameters.

If the observation is made for a short time, the formulas (21) and (25) can not be linearized, so the unknown parameters can not be btained by the regression analysis. In order to solve this problem we adopt the optimization method. Its object function is

$$\min \sum_{i=1}^{n}\left(\{\tilde{u}(t_i)\} - \{u^c(t_i)\}\right)^2 \,. \tag{29}$$

where $\{u^c(t_i)\}$ is the computing displacement vector at the measuring points. Simplifying the formula (29), we obtain

$$f(x)= \sum_{i=1}^{n}\left(\frac{1}{E'(t_i)} - \frac{1}{E_v(t_i)} + \frac{1}{E_v(t_o)}\right)^2 \tag{30}$$

(only considering rheologic factor)

$$f(x)=\sum_{i=1}^{n}\left(\frac{1}{E'(t_i,\alpha_j)} - \alpha_0\left(\frac{1}{E_v(t_i)} - \frac{1}{E_v(t_o)}\right) - \sum_{m=1}^{j}\frac{\alpha_m - \alpha_{m-1}}{E_v(t_i-t_m)}\right)^2 \tag{31}$$

(Considering spatial effect and rheologic factor)

where

$$X = (E_o, E_1, E_2, \eta_1, \eta_2) \tag{32}$$

$E'(t_i)$ and $E'(t_i, \alpha_j)$ are gotten by solving Eq.(20) and (26), $E_v(t_i)$ and $E_v(to)$ are obtained by substituting better x value into the composite modulus chosen model.

The explicit function of formulas (30) and (31) can be established for a specific rheologic model, then the optimal point, or the vector of the viscoelastic parameters tallied with practice, is found by the steps of complex in optimization method.

CHECK AND APPLICATION OF BAM

Two examples are given in this section, firstly, we calculate a typical example, which has theoretic solution using the regular FEM and BAM ,respectly, so as to verify the correctness and reliability of the method and program in the paper. Another is a practical engineering case.

Example 1. A circular tunnel is covered in 50 m deep. The unit weight of the surrounding rock is 0.028 MPa/m,the poisson's ratio is 0.3, The displacement values of measuring points are gotten from the theoretic solution and the model 4 in Table 1 is chosen to operate BA. Its solutions obtainedby different BAM are listed in Table 2 and 3.

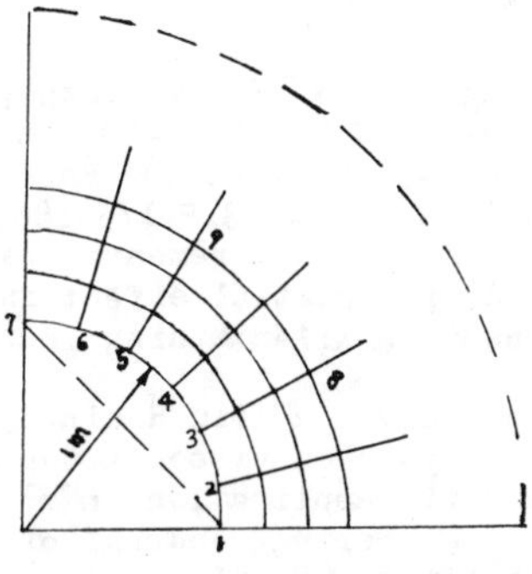

Fig. 1 A quarter circular tunnel and the places of measuring points

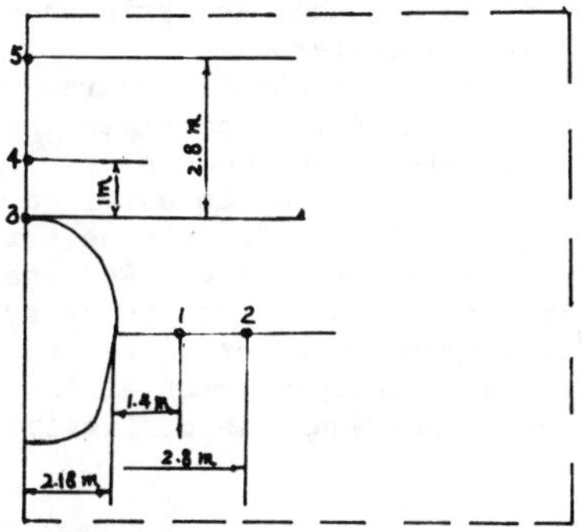

Fig. 2 Measuring section and the places of measuring points

The calculation results show that the parameters values obtained by BA are identical with the theoretic solutions. This illustrates that we can carry out the back analysis and obtain the needfull meachanical parameters of rock mass with the simple convergencemeter or borehole extensometer measurements only after excavation.
From Table 3 we can see that the maximum error of the rheologic parameters E_1, η_1 obtained from combining FEM with the optimization is 9.24% comparing with its theoretic solution. This calculating precision is very good for engineerings.
Example 2. A measuring section of some underground cavern is shown in Fig. 2. The height of overburden is 90 m, and properties of rock mass are : unit weight 0.022 MPa/m, Poission's ratio 0.33, Displacement measurement had been made for a long time and the measuring points had been set up at 0.45 day after excavation. Measuring displacement values are selected within $15.3 \le t \le 141$ day corresponding to the observated datum in situ as the computer input datum of viscoelastic BA, the release coefficients α_1 and α_2 are obtained from incremental BAM [2]. Adopting the regression analysis and the Complex method, respectively, we achieved the back analysis for five-kind rheologic models listed in Table 1, and obtained the initial stress in ground, the elastic modulus and the rheologic parameters of the engineering case. They are listed in Table 4 and 5.
It is most important to give a rough region of the unknown parameters before the back analysis using Complex method. The estimated range for elastic modulus E_0 may be determined from testing value or the value of same rock mass, and the regions of other rheologic parameters are all determined applying the method in reference [3] .
From the results in Table 4 and 5 we think it is suitable for this engineering case to take model 3 or model 4 to describe the features of the viscoelastic deformation of surrounding rock.

CONCLUSION

In this paper we have proposed a BAM of measured rheologic displacement and completed a microcomputer program. Using this method, the initial stress and the elastic and viscoelastic parameters of rock mass can be determined in the light of the measured displacement relevant to time. Its main conclusions are as the follows.

1. As long as there is the observed datum for a longer time, the initial stress and all unknown parameters can be obtained utilizing BAM combined the FEM with the regression analysis and carrying out once the whole analytic process. So the method saves time and fund, and a small quantity of compute is done only. For the BAM combined FEM with optimization, iterative operation is needed. However, on condition that there is only a small amount of measured material in a short time, the fundamental parameters fit in practice can all be gotten.

2. Measuring points are set up as soon as possible after excavation, and the more the measuring number of times and the longer the time, the nearer to

true values the back analysis ones of rheologic parameters.

3. The back analysis program completed can be used to consider the back analysis of the models of five kinds. Besides, BAM is combined with elastic, elastoplastic, viscoelastic and viscoelastic-plastic FEM analysis to form a completely analysing system.

4. The proposed method remain to be further developed, such as the viscoplastic back analysis of displacement.

REFERENCES

1 S. Sakurai & K. Takeuchi, Back analysis of measured displacements of tunnels, Rock Mechanics and Rock Engineering, Vol. 16, No.3, P.173-180, 1983.

2 Wang Zhiyin, Incremental back analysis considering spatial effect in underground Opening, Xi'an Mining Institute, 1987.3.

3 Wang Zhiyin & Liu Huaiheng, Finite element analysis on viscoelastoplastic behavior and its application in rock mechanics and engineering, Journal of Xi'an Mining Institute, No. 1, 1985.

Table 1 The composite modulus and viscous modulus of viscoelastic models

Model	Creep formula	Composite modulus	Viscous modulus
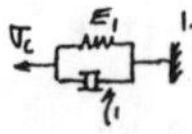 1.	$\varepsilon^v = \frac{\sigma_c}{E_1}(1-e^{-\frac{E_1}{\eta_1}t})$	$E_1/(1-e^{-\frac{E_1}{\eta_1}t})$	$E_1/(1-e^{-\frac{E_1}{\eta_1}t})$
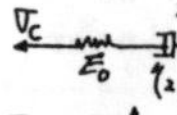 2.	$\varepsilon^v = \sigma_c(\frac{t}{\eta_2}+\frac{1}{E_0})$	$E_0\eta_2/(E_0 t+\eta_2)$	η_2/t
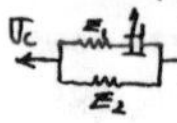 3.	$\varepsilon^v = \frac{\sigma_c}{E_2}(1-\frac{E_1}{E_0}e^{-\frac{E_1E_2}{E_0\eta_1}t})$ ($E_0 = E_1+E_2$)	$E_2/(1-\frac{E_1}{E_0}e^{-\frac{E_1E_2}{E_0\eta_1}t})$	$E_2E_0/E_1(1-e^{-\frac{E_1E_2}{E_0\eta_1}t})$
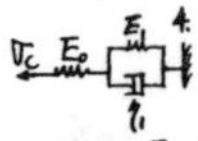 4.	$\varepsilon^v = \frac{\sigma_c}{E_1}(\frac{E_0+E_1}{E_0}-e^{-\frac{E_1}{\eta_1}t})$	$E_1/(\frac{E_1+E_0}{E_0}-e^{-\frac{E_1}{\eta_1}t})$	$E_1/(1-e^{-\frac{E_1}{\eta_1}t})$
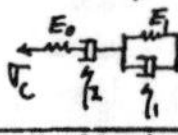 5.	$\varepsilon^v = \frac{\sigma_c}{E_1}(\frac{E_1}{E_0}+\frac{E_1 t}{\eta_2}+(1-e^{-\frac{E_1}{\eta_1}t}))$	$E_1/(\frac{E_1}{E_0}+\frac{E_1 t}{\eta_2}+(1-e^{-\frac{E_1}{\eta_1}t}))$	$E_1/(\frac{E_1 t}{\eta_2}+(1-e^{-\frac{E_1}{\eta_1}t}))$

* Using formula (7) for model 1, let $E_0 \to \infty$ to obtain $E_v(t)$.

Table 2 The BA results combined FEM with regression analysis

BA parameters	Measuring point number or line 2, 3, 4, 5, 6 — BA measuring instantaneous displacements	Measuring point number or line 1-7, 3-8, 5-9 — BA measuring relative rheologic displacements	Theoretic Values
σ_{x0} (MPa)	-1.40002	-1.40003	-1.40000
τ_{xy0} (MPa)	0.00002	0.00004	0.00000
E_0 (MPa)	2100.18000	2099.93200	2100.00000
E_1 (MPa)	/	43236.73100	46300.00000
η_1 (Pa.s)	/	5.9178×10^{15}	5.9240×10^{15}
Maximum error	0.00875 %	6.61 %	

Table 3 The BA results combined FEM with optimization method

BA parameters	Distributive region of parameters	BA measuring rheologic displacements	Theoretic value
σ_{x0} (MPa)	/	-1.40003	-1.40000
τ_{xy0} (MPa)	/	0.00004	0.00000
E_1 (MPa)	(30000, 50000)	43707.5200	46300.00000
η_1 (Pa.s)	(4.752×10^{15} , 6.480×10^{15})	5.4897×10^{15}	5.9240×10^{15}
Maximum error	/	9.24 %	/

Table 4 The BA results combined FEM with regression analysis

BA parameters	BA Values Model 1.	Model 2.	Model 3.	Model 4.
σ_{x0} (MPa)	-3.5258	-3.5258	-3.5258	-3.5258
σ_{y0} (MPa)	-1.9980	-1.9980	-1.9980	-1.9980
τ_{xy0} (MPa)	-0.8802	-0.8802	-0.8802	-0.8802
E_0 (MPa)	/	66.6667	84.9688	75.7838
E_1 (MPa)	348.8973	/	16.6404	348.8973
E_2 (MPa)	/	/	68.3280	/
η_1 (10^{15} Pa.s)	0.6344	/	0.0243	0.6344
η_2 (10^{15} Pa.s)	/	4.2300	/	/
Relative coefficient R*	0.9368	0.6302	0.9368	0.9368

* The closer to one the value R, the better the results of regression.

Table 5 The BA results combined FEM with optimization method

BA Parameters	Distributive region of parameters	BA results Model 1.	Model 2.	Model 3	Model 4.	Model 5
σ_{x0} (MPa)	/	-3.5258	-3.5258	-3.5258	-3.5258	-3.5258
σ_{y0} (MPa)	/	-1.9980	-1.9980	-1.9980	-1.9980	-1.9980
τ_{xy0} (MPa)	/	-0.8802	-0.8802	-0.8802	-0.8802	-0.8802
E_0 (MPa)	(36,210)	/	61.4049	137.2194	197.4008	192.7803
E_1 (MPa)	(15,349)	144.0043	/	28.6404	166.3335	144.0039
E_2 (MPa)	(21,180)	/	/	108.5873	/	/
η_1 (10^{15} Pa.s)	(0.025,0.343)	0.0501	/	0.2600	0.1298	0.0528
η_2 (10^{15} Pa.s)	(0.686,5.253)	/	5.2103	/	/	1.1132

Numerical Methods in Geomechanics (Innsbruck 1988), Swoboda (ed.)
© 1989 Balkema, Rotterdam. ISBN 90 6191 809 X

A visco-plastic FEM analysis for the stability of slope in the anisotropic swelling soil

Ning Li
Department of Hydroelectric Engineering, Shaanxi Institute of Mechanic Engineering, Xi'an, People's Republic of China

ABSTRACT: A FEM analysis with considerations of swell, joint and creep behaviors of soil is described in this paper to simulate the procedure of the landslides along the experimental channel on the expansive soil. A compare between the computation results and in - situ measurements at the experimental channel is illustrated.

1 INTRODUCTION

In Henan province of China, an experimental channel was built in the swelling soil area in 1984 in order to study the behavior of slope stability of swelling soil. For a large channel project will be constructed soon in the same area.

Many landslides have occurred along the experimental channel by now. And all of them happened during the rainy period and only at the places where the joints are crowded and developed.

The joints are filled with white grey mud which will swell when the water content of the mud increase. The in-situ measurements demonstrate that the main factors affecting slope stability are swell and joint. To simulate the procedure and analyse the mechanism of landslide, a numerical simulating analysis was done for three sections along the experimental channel.

2. SOME CONSIDERATIONS ABOUT THE MECH. MODEL

2.1 Swelling model for the expansive soil

The laboratory test illustrates that the swelling deformation not only depends on the contents of expansive materials but also on the water contents and stress states of the soil. The relationship between the swelling deformation and pressure is shown in Figure 1 and eq.(1)

$$\varepsilon^s = A.\ln \frac{P_{max}}{\sigma} \quad \text{when} \quad 0<\sigma<P_{max} \qquad (1)$$

where

A is the coefficient of swelling deformation and P_{max} is the maximum swelling pressure under which the swelling deformation is just restricted to zero. Both A and P_{max} can be determined by laboratory test. Here we obtained

$$A = a + b\,(w - w_o)$$

$$P_{max} = a_1 + b_1 w_o + c_1 w_o^2$$

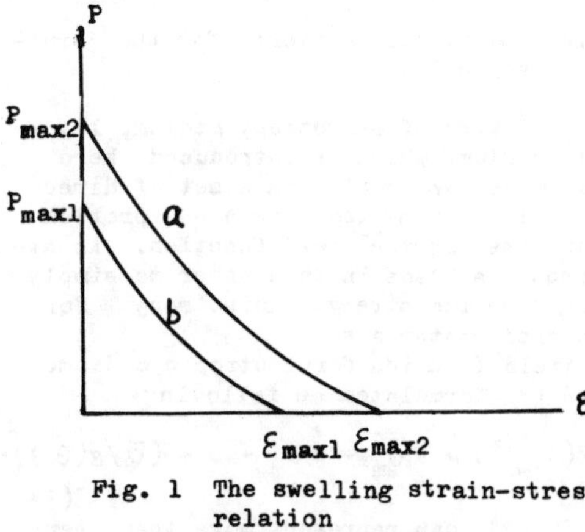

Fig. 1 The swelling strain-stress relation
a. normal to joints
b. parallel to joints

where

a, b, a_1, b_1 and c_1 are coefficients of curve fitting to the experiment results.

And w is the current water content while w_o is the initial water content of the soil.

In case of soil with a set of directional joint system, the similar eqs. can be established in the directions of normal to and tangential to joint plane respectively by the proper tests.

Soil is known as a kind of frictional materials. The swelling of soil volume will result in the diminution of its shearing strength (σ_f). Figure 2 and Eq.(2) is a swelling-soften model put forward in this paper to describe the swelling-soften behavior of the soil.

$$\sigma_f = \sigma_{fo} - k \cdot \varepsilon^s \quad (2)$$

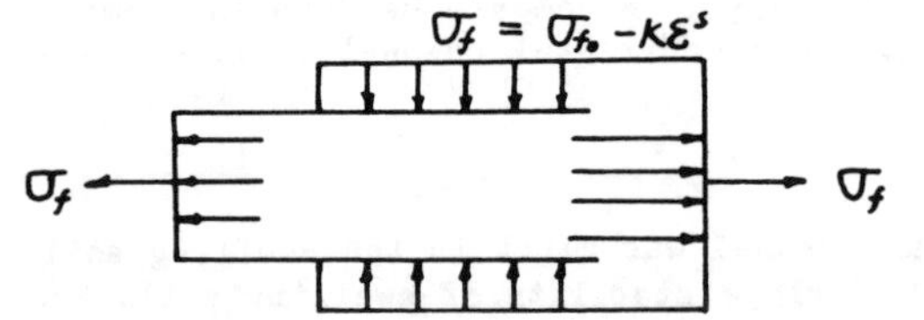

Fig. 2 The swelling-softening model

The above softening coefficients K , however, can hardly be determined directly, because the swelling-shearing test is difficulty to do. The method to determine K used in this paper is indirect. By the means of math. method, the two common test results are combined to determine K .

2.2 The plastic criteria for the jointed soil

As a kind of anisotropy medium, layered medium, which is introduced here to model the soil with a set of directional joint system , is a new problem for its plastic yield function. An attempt is made in this paper to simply describe the strength anisotropy for layered materials.

Yield function for isotropic medium can be formulated as following.

$$F(\sigma_m, \bar{\sigma}) = a\sigma_m^2 + b\sigma_m + c + (\bar{\sigma}/g(\theta))^n \quad (3)$$

Eq.(3) can represent more than ten kinds of yield functions by giving a, b, c, n and θ different values.

For layered soil, which has different plastic limits in each directions and should have an anisotropic yield surface imaged in anisotropic stress space which can hardly be expressed by math., a transformation of stress space is introduced in this paper from anisotropy to isotropy. Let

$$\sigma'_x = \sigma_x , \quad \sigma'_z = \sigma_z \quad (4)$$

$$\sigma'_y = \sigma_y / k_1 , \quad \tau'_{xy} = \tau_{xy}/K_2$$

where

$$k_1 = (C_x - \sigma'_y \cdot tg\,\phi_x)/(C_y - \sigma'_x \cdot tg\,\phi_y)$$

$$k_2 = C_x / C_y$$

$\underline{\sigma}$ is the stress vector in isotropic stress space.

$\underline{\sigma}'$ is the stress vector in anisotropic stress space.

k_1 and k_2 are the transformation coefficients.

And

C_x, C_y is the conhesion and ϕ_x , ϕ_y is the friction angle in each direction respectively.

In transformed stress space, the shape of anisotropic yield surface will approximately be the same as the one of isotropic yield surface. That is

$$F'(\sigma'_m, \bar{\sigma}') = F(\sigma_m, \bar{\sigma}) \quad (5)$$

2.3 The visco-plastic model for layered soil

It is believed to all that soil has creep behavior and it is well proved here by the in-situ measures. Figure 3 is the Bingham model to be used here to describe the visco-plastic behavior of the soil. The relation is as following

$$\sigma = \begin{cases} 0 & \text{when } \sigma \leq \sigma_f \\ \eta\dot{\varepsilon} & \text{when } \sigma > \sigma_f \end{cases} \quad (6)$$

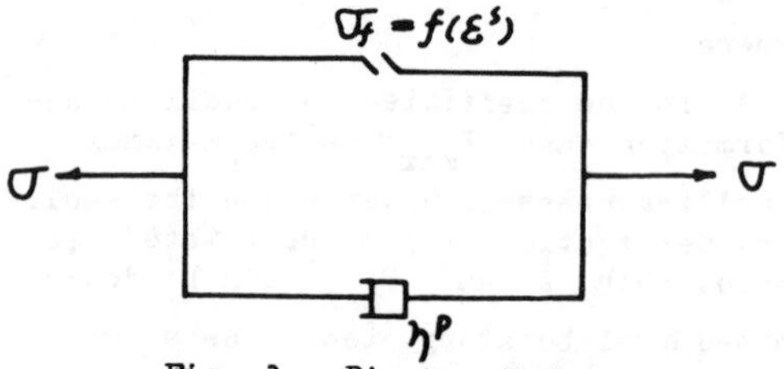

Fig. 3 Bingham Model

For two dimensions, the eq.(6) can be written as following.

$$\dot{\underset{\sim}{\varepsilon}}^{vp} = \frac{1}{\eta^p} \cdot F \cdot \frac{\partial F}{\partial \underset{\sim}{\sigma}} \quad (F > 0) \qquad (7)$$

where

η^p is the visco-plastic parameter and F is the yield function ; $\frac{\partial F}{\partial \underset{\sim}{\sigma}}$ represents the flowing direction of visco-plastic strain when the associated flow rule is introduced here.

For layered medium, a development on eq. (7) is made in Ref. [1] by author. It is as following.

$$\dot{\underset{\sim}{\varepsilon}}^{vp} = F' \cdot \underset{\sim}{R} \cdot \frac{\partial F'}{\partial \underset{\sim}{\sigma}} \qquad (8)$$

where

$\underset{\sim}{R}$ is a diagonal matrix of the anisotropic visco-plastic parameters.

$$\underset{\sim}{R} = \begin{bmatrix} 1/\eta_1^p & 0 & 0 \\ 0 & 1/\eta_2^p & 0 \\ 0 & 0 & 1/\eta_3^p \end{bmatrix}$$

in which

η_1^p, η_2^p and η_3^p are the visco-plastic parameters in the direction of parallel to, normal to and taugent to layered face respectively. And F' is the yield function for layered medium.

The visco-plastic strain increments can be obtained by the "forward difference method" to the eq.(8).

$$\Delta \underset{\sim}{\varepsilon}^{vp} = \dot{\underset{\sim}{\varepsilon}}^{vp} \cdot \Delta t = \Delta t . F' . \underset{\sim}{R} . \frac{\partial F'}{\partial \underset{\sim}{\sigma}} \qquad (9)$$

$$(F > 0)$$

The price for the simplicity and clarity of the "forward difference method" is that eq. (9) is conditional stable. The maximum time step is given by Cormeau [2].

2.4 The assumption for FEM analysis

The stress states for every element at any time step after excavation are no more than three

a. elastic state $\underset{\sim}{\varepsilon} = \underset{\sim}{\varepsilon}^e = \underset{\sim}{D}^{-1} \cdot \underset{\sim}{\sigma}$

b. swelling state $\underset{\sim}{\varepsilon} = \underset{\sim}{\varepsilon}^e + \underset{\sim}{\varepsilon}^s$

c. swelling-creep state $\underset{\sim}{\varepsilon} = \underset{\sim}{\varepsilon}^e + \underset{\sim}{\varepsilon}^s + \underset{\sim}{\varepsilon}^{vp}$

The swelling coefficient A and the maximum swelling pressure P_{max} vary with the water content w, while w varies with the rainfall, which can be formulated as

$$w = f(t) = a_o + b_o t + c_o t^2$$

by in-situ measurements.

Assumed it to be a kind of pore pressure, the swelling pressure P is subtracted from the total stress to obtain the effective stress to perform the calculation.

The "initial-visco-strain increment method" is efficiently used here.

3. THE COMPUTATION RESULTS

3.1 Section C-C

There are vary few joints in this section. Therefore an isotropy assumption can be made and the basic parameters are

$E = 96.48$ kg/cm^2 $\quad \mu = 0.219$

$C_o = 0.31$ kg/cm^2 , $\phi_o = 21.8^o$

$\eta^p = 4.11 \times 10^5$ day. kg/cm^2

slope angle is 1: 2.0

The stresses at the measuring point 56 and 58 are shown in Figure 4 and the displacement of point C_I is in Figure 5. The computation results are quite approaching to the in-situ measurements. And both predict that the slope is stable.

3.2 Section B-B

There are two sets of joints in B-B section, which are nearly symmetrical about the vertical axis. Only the second set of joints parallel to the slope is considered in computation. And the anisotropic behaviors have to be considered equally. The parameters for computation are

$C_1 = 0.25$ kg/cm^2, $\phi_1 = 16.6^o$

$C_2 = 0.17$ kg/cm^2 , $\phi_2 = 12.0^o$

$\eta_1^p = 4.22 \times 10^5$ day.kg/cm^2

$\eta_2^p = 2.11 \times 10^5$ day.kg/cm^2

slope angle is 1:2.5 and joint angle is 30°

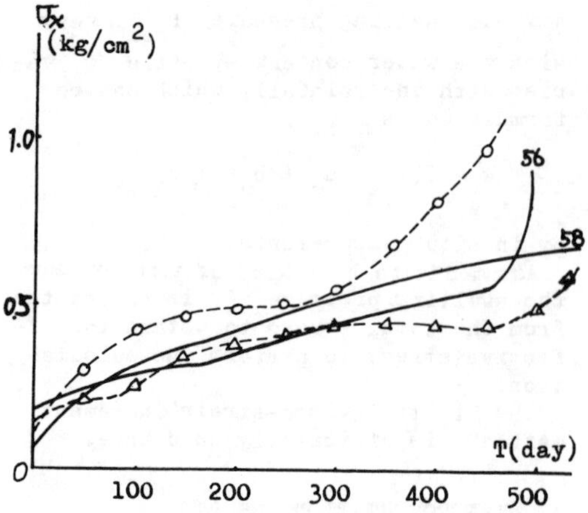

Fig. 4 The stresses in section C-C

o stands for the measured stress of point 56

Δ stands for the measured stress of point 58

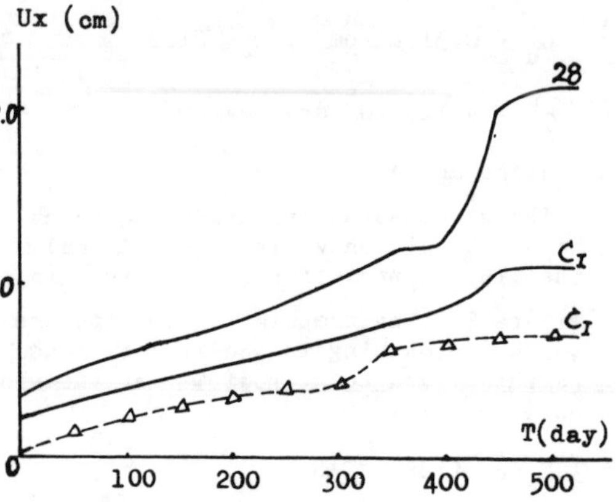

Fig. 5 The displacements in section C - C

Δ stands forthe measured displacement of point C_I

Figure 6 shows the displacements at B_I and B_{II} . Both computation results and in-situ measurements demonstrate that the slope will slide after eight months from excavation.

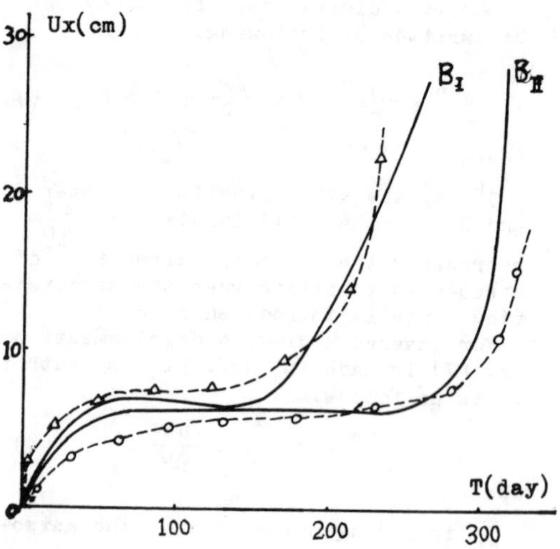

Fig. 6 The displacements of section B-B

o Stands for the measured displacement of point B_I

Δ stands for the measured displacemtnt of B_{II}

3.3 Section A - A

The computation conditions in section A-A is very similar to those in section B-B except for

$$C_1 = 0.25 \text{ kg/cm}^2, \quad \phi_1 = 17.5^\circ$$

$$C_2 = 0.19 \text{ kg/cm}^2, \quad \phi_2 = 14.4^\circ$$

$$\eta_1^P = 2.11 \times 10^6 \text{ day.kg/cm}^2,$$

$$\eta_2^P = 1.04 \times 10^6 \text{ day.kg/cm}^2 \text{ and}$$

slope angle is 1:3.0 .

Figure 7 illustrate the stresses at point 6 and 9 and Figure 8 shows the displacements at the point A_I and A_{II}. The computation results predict that the slope will slide 20 months later from excavation while the practical slope of the channel slid in Nov.1986, 32 months later from excavation. The explanation has been made for the delay of sliding. The reason may be that the practical section of the channel has become 3° gentlerin slope and 1.8 M shallower in depth than the designed section by the wash of rainfall.

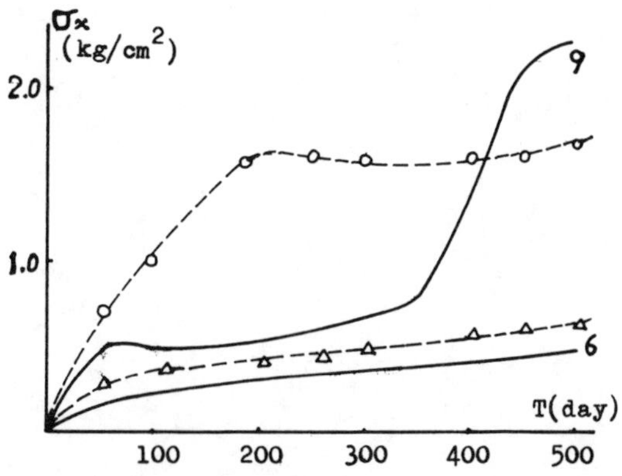

Fig. 7 The stresses in section A-A

Δ stands for the measured stress of point 6

o stands for the measured stress of point 9

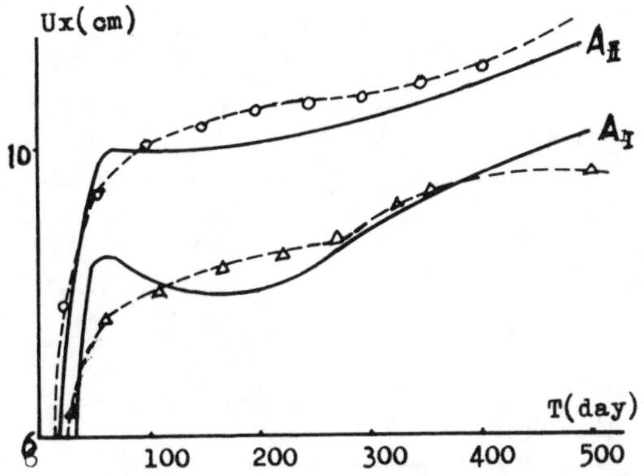

Fig. 8 The displacements in section A-A

Δ stands for the measured displacement of point A_I

o stands for the measured displacement of point A_{II}

4. CONCLUSIONS

4.1 There are many factors affecting slope stability. The most important one is the strength C and ϕ. Because the strength will fall down (soften) when swell, the properties of swelling, softening and the water contents will all affect the stability of the slope in the swelling soil.

4.2 Swelling depends on stress state and water content. It is specially significant for the problem of stability of slope discussed in this paper to consider swelling behavior of soil, because the initial stress in the soil is not large enough to restrict the swelling, for the slope is not high enough.

4.2 The computation results also demonstrate that it is important to consider the joints for slope stability analysis.

4.4 The creep properties of soil have a direct effect on the time of sliding. The strength softening resulting from swelling will accelerate creep deformation, which results in slope sliding.

REFERENCES

Zhang Haidong and Lining, A Visco-Elastic and Visco-Plastic FEM analysis for underground openings in layered rock, proceedings of the international symposium on engineering in complex rock formations, pp.552-557. 1986.11.

1. Cormeau, Numerical Stability in Quasi-Static Elasto/visco-plasticity, Int. J. Numerical Methods Engrg. Vol.9. 1975.

Numerical Methods in Geomechanics (Innsbruck 1988), Swoboda (ed.)
© 1989 Balkema, Rotterdam. ISBN 90 6191 809 X

The method of decoupled finite elements as auxiliary device for the analysis of a damage

H.Geisler & A.Papassotiriou
Beton- und Monierbau Gesellschaft m.b.H., Innsbruck, Austria

ABSTRACT: Modern tunnelling, as it is presently being applied with great success according to the New Austrian Tunnelling Method (NATM) for a number of tunnel advances, is also characterized by various damages. It is important and essential for the application and further development of this construction method to clarify damages which occured by finding out the reasons for these damages and by informing experts accordingly. The present paper deals with the numerical stability analysis of a special damage which occured on a tunnel driven according to NATM.

1 PRELIMINARY HISTORY AND INTRODUCTION

At a construction section, where driving works of the crown could be carried out without problems and without noticeable geological or rock-mechanical changes, driving works of the bench took place several weeks later. In the course of these works, a stability failure occured, manifesting itself in the cracking of the shotcrete lining of the already supported tunnel cross-section, going hand in hand with considerable settlements of the crown arch of up to 80 cms. This deformation process could be stopped only by initiating as quickly as possible the remucking of the bench and by installing a support of the crown arch.

Fig. 1: Supported state of damage

Fig. 1 shows this state of damage with remucked bench and supported crown arch thereupon. It is obvious that such an event was reason enough to check all aspects with regard to the liability of the construction method and of the structural safety.

For this purpose, a comprehensive analysis of damages was carried out, including computations with the target of obtaining a numerical judgment of the loss in stability.

In this connection, a computation model had to be set up, making it possible to represent the rock-mechanical reality and its connection with the damage in question as closely as possible to reality.

2 ROCK-MECHANICAL REALITY AND GENERAL IMPRESSION AND STATE OF DAMAGE

In the course of crown- and bench advance, the geology encountered showed an almost horizontally layered rock.

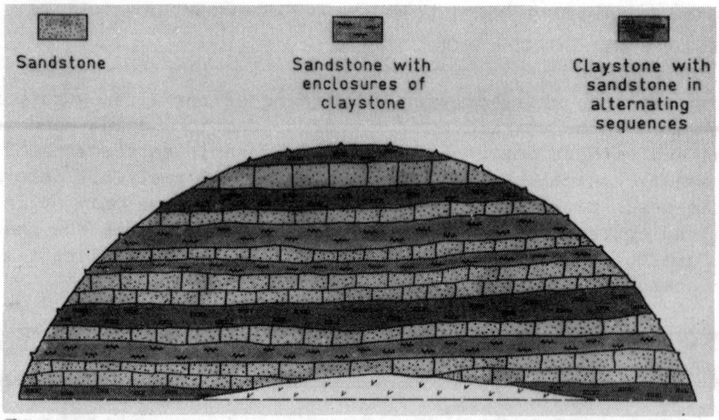

Fig. 2: Geology (crown)

The geology encountered results from Fig.2, where alternating sequences of bedded sandstone and slaty enclosures of claystone and sandstone characterized the structure of the layers. Apart from individual large cracks with openings of up to 2 mms, medium-sized cracks showed mean to wide distances. On the whole, the number of cracks was considered to be small.

Apart from a few spots where water penetrated, the construction section where the damages occured later on was dry, so that the rock was also not subjected to changes due to water seepage.

The mechanical properties of the rock corresponded to the estimates prognosticated. These estimates were based on comprehensive and thorougly evaluated results of preliminary investigations.

Following rock characteristics applied:

Sandstone:	γ	= 23 kN/m3
	E_v	= 1900 - 22500 MN/m2
	ν	= 0,1 - 0,5
	σ_D	= 10 - 30 MN/m2
	σ_Z	= 0,1 - 5 MN/m2
Claystone:	γ	= 23,5 kN/m3
	E_v	= 10 - 160 MN/m2
	ν	= 0,1 - 0,5
	σ_D	= 0,2 - 3,0 MN/m2
	σ_Z	= 0,1 - 3,9 MN/m2

The values of the shear strength in the planes of weakness were as follows:

	on bedding planes	on joint planes
Sandstone	$\varphi_s' = 30^\circ$ $c_s' = 0$	$\varphi_k = 35^\circ$ $c_k = 0$
Sandstone with enclosures of claystone	$\varphi_s' = 25^\circ$ $c_s' = 0$	$\varphi_k = 30^\circ$ $c_k = 0$
Claystone with sandstone in alternating sequences	$\varphi_s' = 15^\circ$ (10) $c_s' = 0$	$\varphi_k' = 20^\circ$ (10) $c_k' = 0$

After the damage had occured and as soon as the required emergency- and support measures had been finished, the entire area of damage was subjected to a close investigation.

A variety of damage characteristics showed, collected in Fig. 2 in a general impression and state of damage.

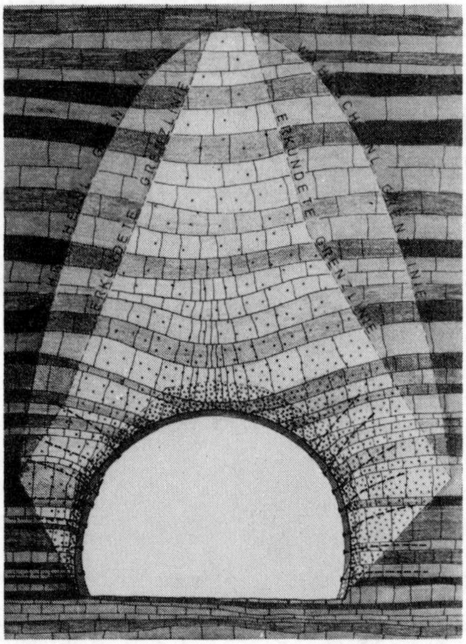

Fig. 3: General impression and state of damage

This general impression and state of damage conveyed a ruptured rock around and above the tunnel on the one hand and a cracked shotcrete lining on the other hand.

The state of failure of the rock is characterized by loosened rock zones behind the side walls, a wedge-like rock sagging above the tunnel with bendings and displacements of layers, as well as an entirely undisturbed floor without any indication whatsoever of the action of force.

On the shotcrete lining, shear failures showed both in the area of the crown springs and in the area of the side walls. The shear failures represented damage characteristics which were in kinematic agreement with the settlement of the crown arch. The impression and state of damage pointed towards a failure mechanism originally caused by a loss in stability of the rock-bearing ring.

This final conclusion was derived from the fact that the shotcrete lining did show damages both in the crown and in the side walls, which could have been caused by excessive loading only. This excessive loading could have originated from the rock only and only then, when the rock-bearing ring, obviously adjusted in the course of driving the crown and still stable when the crown was driven already, suddenly lost its bearing capacity during driving works of the bench.

Possibly responsible for the loss in stability of the rock-bearing ring were planes of weakness of the rock mass, running parallel to the tunnel axis, dipping towards the tunnel from behind the side walls, as well as a particularly brittle behaviour of the rock.

Bearing in mind the structure of the planes of weakness, the general state of damage, as well as the explanation of the failure mechanism, the basis for the setting-up of a realistic computation model was given.

3 COMPUTATION MODEL

In the present case, a two-dimensional model was selected, representing an infinite half-space and discreted by finite elements, as can be seen from Fig. 4.

The finite-elements-mesh is partly composed of LINEAR-VARYING-STRAIN-TRIANGULAR-ELEMENTS (LST-elements (1), (2) and partly of PLANE-QUADRATIC-BOUNDARY-ELEMENTS (PQB-elements) (3), (4)).

Elements of the LST-type comprised the area around the excavation edge, corresponding to approximately the 2,5 fold of the tunnel diameter, whereas the elements of the PQB-type described the area of the infinite half-space reaching beyond that area. Both the element types mentioned were based on a quadratic shape-function.

The shotcrete lining, representing the tunnel support, was discreted by BEAM-elements. The compound-condition of the system rock/support was established along the excavation edge by coupling the joints of the BEAM-elements (5) with the corresponding joints of the LST-elements.

Proceeding from the objective to realize a realistic stability calculation as possible, it was necessary to integrate the anisotropy and the discontinuity of the rock in the computation model.

In order to achieve this objective, the mesh of the LST-elements was approximately adjusted to the real geometry of the planes of weakness on the one hand and on the other hand, so-called "CONSTRAIN-JOINT-ELEMENTS" (COJO-elements) (6) (Fig. 5) were provided for within the joints of the LST-elements.

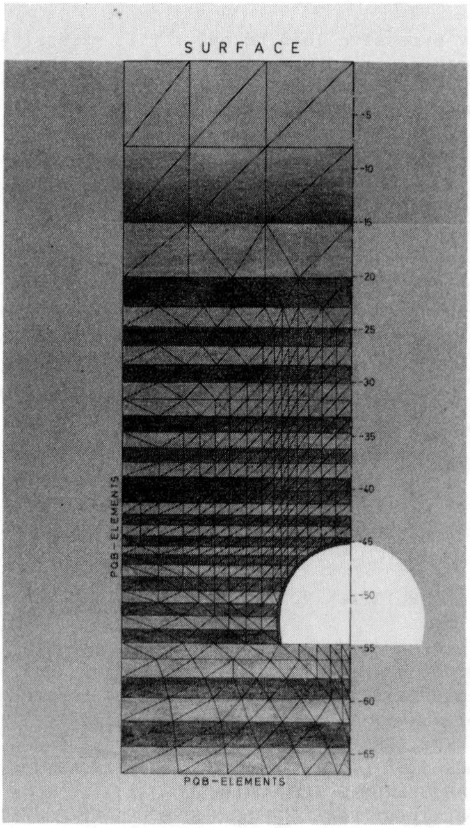

Fig. 4: Infinite half-space, discreted by finite elements

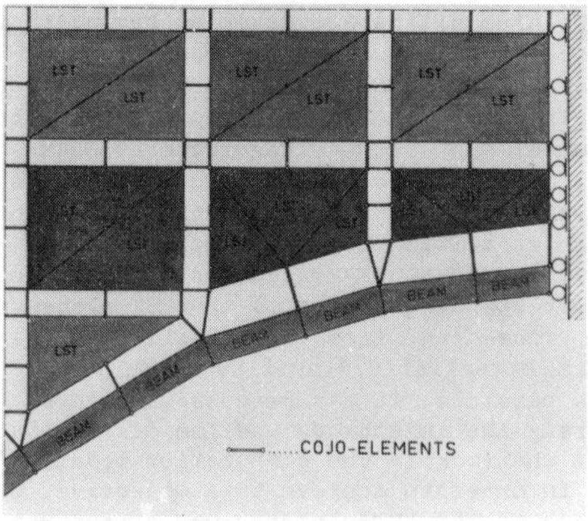

Fig. 5: Detail of the FE-mesh with COJO-elements

By adjusting the LST-elements-mesh to the real horizontal geometry of the planes of weakness and by arranging the COJO-elements, it was possible to take into account both changes in the stability and in the deformation properties within the sequence of layers. It was thus also possible to make allowance for the physical reality that planes of weakness, in accordance with their respective loaction, do bring about a decrease in the strength properties and simultaneously an increase in the deformability of the rock mass.

This simulation could be achieved by supplying the LST-elements, corresponding to a geological layer, with the respective material characteristics and by supplying the element joints, located on a bedding plane or on a joint plane, with a state of displacement (Fig. 6) by means of the COJO-elements. This state could be determined either as "FIXSTATE", "FREESTATE", or "SLIPSTATE".

$$\{\Delta\}^K = \begin{cases} \Delta_s^K \text{ ..... TANGENTIAL DISPLACEMENT} \\ \Delta_n^K \text{ ..... NORMAL DISPLACEMENT} \end{cases}$$

$$\{\lambda\}^K = \begin{cases} \lambda_s^K \text{ ..... SHEAR FORCE} \\ \lambda_n^K \text{ ..... NORMAL FORCE} \end{cases}$$

$$F_z^K = \sigma_z^K \cdot L \cdot D$$

$$F_t^K = \tau_{GL}^K \cdot L \cdot D \cdot \frac{\lambda_s^K}{|\lambda_s^K|}$$

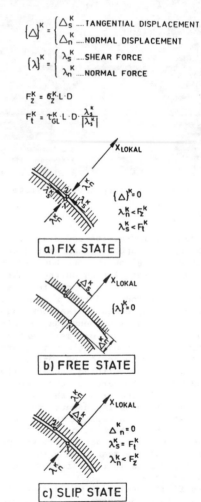

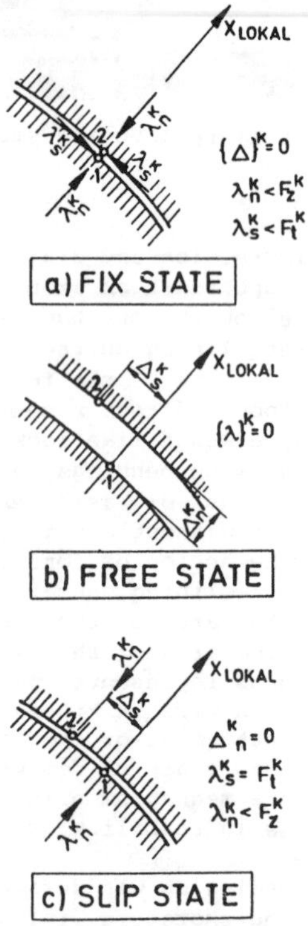

Fig. 6: State of displacement of COJO-elements

The COJO-element is not a joint element in the proper sense of the word (7), (8), however, this element serves the simulation of conditions in planes of weakness, enforcing a certain state of stress and deformation. It is therefore a question of a "control element", leading to the required coupling or decoupling within adjoining finite elements when computing the total stiffness matrix. So as to fix the forces F_z^k and F_t^k, the angle of friction φ^k and the cohesion c^k as well as the tensile strength σ_z^k have to be given.

Within the computation procedure, either the Mohr-Coulomb shear strength criterion or a tensile failure criterion in the planes of weakness are being described. (Fig. 7)

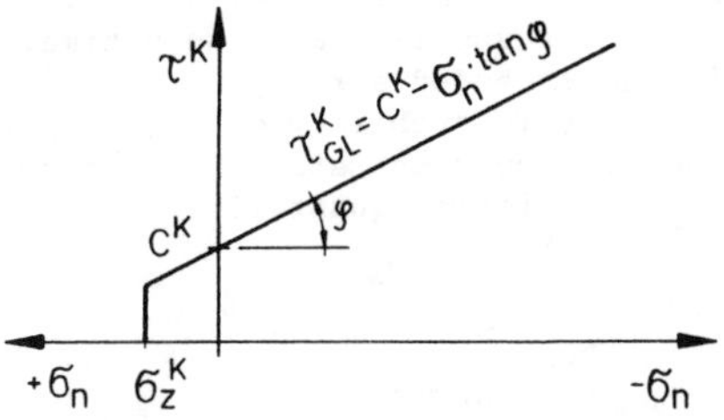

$$\text{COULOMB:}\quad F_Z^K = \tau_{GL}^K \cdot L \cdot D \cdot \frac{\lambda_S^K}{|\lambda_S^K|}$$

$$\text{TENSION:}\quad F_t^K = \sigma_Z^K \cdot L \cdot D$$

Fig. 7: Coulomb's friction law and tensile failure criterion

Within the framework of the computation programme applied here (9) allowance was made for the fact that irreversible deformations do occur, when the shear strength and/or the tensile strength in planes of weakness are being exceeded in situ. It was arranged that any exceeding of the shear failure criterion and the tensile strength criterion respectively led to a decoupling of the corresponding LST-elements and thus to an actualization and re-computation of the total stiffness matrix.

By a number of iterations allowance is made for the fact that a state of equilibrium always occurs in situ in case of planes of weakness, as long as a redistribution of stress to adjoining areas is possible for local strength exceedings. If a state of equilibrium is impossible, the computation procedure does not find a convergency and gives reason to reconsider the dimensioning of the tunnel lining.

In literature (10) this method is known as "DECOUPLED FINITE ELEMENT METHOD". It is particularly apt to describe failures in layered and jointed rock.

Due to the fact that the data can be regarded as approximately symmetrical, the computation model was chosen symmetrically to the vertical tunnel axis in order to simplify the scope of the computation.

4 COMPUTATION RESULTS

4.1 Test computations

Before the computation model described was applied with regard to the actual damage, two test computations were realized. These computations aimed particularly at checking the general deformation behaviour of the computation model by means of plausibility controls.

In a first test run, the behaviour of the model was at first investigated on the theoretical example of full-face excavation and immediate shotcrete support, without assuming a shear strength and a tensile strength within the bedding planes and joint planes. In a second test run, the computation was realized on the same theoretical example as in test run 1, however, under the assumption that the excavation edge remained unsupported.

It was the objective of the two test computations to find out how many iteration loops were required to prove numerically a stable state of deformation in case of a supported excavation edge and an unstable state of deformation in case of an unsupported excavation edge respectively.

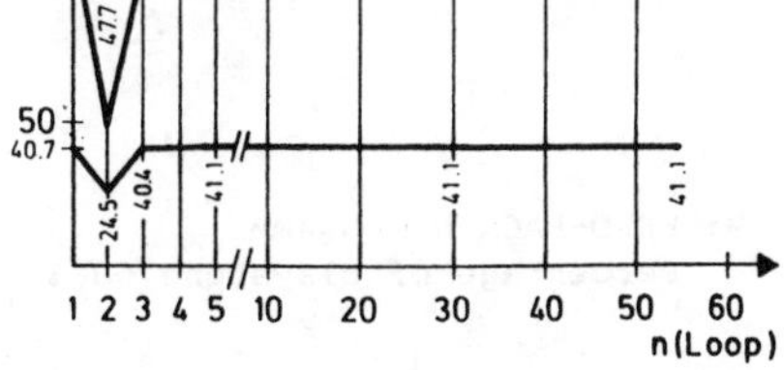

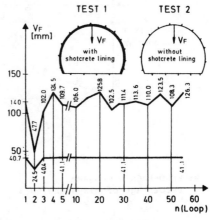

Fig. 8: Computation result for test runs 1 and 2 Roof deformation V_R dependent upon the number of loops

As can be seen from Fig. 8, a stable roof deformation V_R could be stated after three loops already, whereas with regard to test run 2, a tendency towards a stabilization of the deformation V_R could not even be stated after 55 loops. The roof deformation V_R, changing from loop to loop without a downward tendency, indicated the instability criterion.

4.2 Ultimate load calculation

As pointed out at the beginning of this paper, it was the objective of the damage analysis to gain a numerical judgment of the loss in stability. An ultimate load calculation was carried out, applying the computation model described and making allowance for the criteria required for a back analysis.

The computation result obtained with respect to the failure of the shotcrete structure was gathered in a graph, denominated by the authors as "FEED-BACK-NOMOGRAM". (Fig. 9)

pendent upon the relationship of the moduli of elasticity between claystone and sandstone, were put into relation to the ultimate load (n_u, m_u) of the shotcrete lining.

Using the roof deformation V_R as initial parameter - in our example V_R amounted to 30 mm - the respective relationship of the moduli of elasticity between claystone and sandstone and subsequently also the shell forces |min n|, |max m| and |min m| respectively, corresponding to the actual case, can be read from the nomogram. In the left-hand upper quadrant of the nomogram it is thus being checked whether or not the ultimate load of the shotcrete lining - 27 cm thick for instance - has not yet been reached, has just been reached, or has been exceeded already.

As can be seen from Fig. 9, it turned out that in our special case the ultimate load had been exceeded already.

The loss in stability of the shotcrete structure could therefore be considered to be numerically quantified.

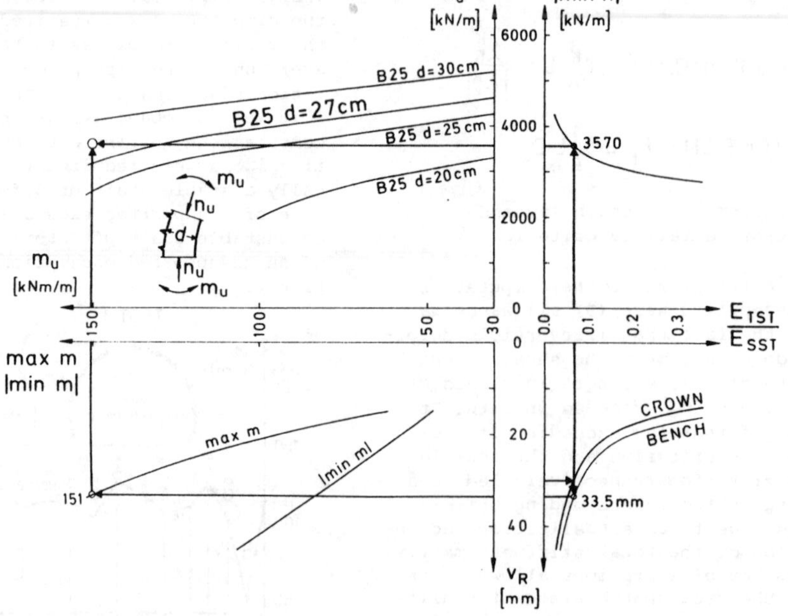

Fig. 9: FEED-BACK-NOMOGRAMM
Percentage of claystone 50 %

In this nomogram, the shell forces |min n|, |max m| and |min m| respectively as well as the roof deformation V_R, de-

5 CONCLUDING REMARKS

In connection with a damage which occured during construction works of a large railway tunnel, a back analysis was carried out, aiming at obtaining a numerical judgment of the loss in stability.

The marginal conditions, as f.i. structure of the rock, rockmechanical characteristics, support resistance, as well as the measuring results gained from in situ measurements, observed for such computation tasks during tunnel driving works, were supplemented in this special case by the fact that the ultimate load of the shotcrete lining had been exceeded. With respect to the realization of a realistic stability computation, this fact offered a criterion which was apt to confirm the key parameter responsible for the loss in stability.

The geological structure of the rock was represented by a finite-element-mesh which permitted to determine the obvious, however, to a certain extent regular anisotropy and discontinuity of the rock, in the best way possible. Otherwise, however, the computation introduced was based on the assumption of an intact rock. Possible discontinuities due to tectonic influences, which cannot be excluded, have not been taken into consideration when setting up this computation model.

By application of the Decoupled Finite Elements Method (DFEM), allowance was made for the fact of the loosening of the rock as a consequence of tunnel driving works. Within the framework of the back analysis desribed here, above all an explanation was sought for the loss in ultimate load of the shotcrete lining. It was of particular interest to determine the probable rock parameter, responsible for the loss in stability of the support structure. The geological structure of the rock, explored during tunnel driving works, the roof deformation measured when driving the crown, as well as the ultimate load of the shotcrete lining, served as key criteria for a realistic computation.

The computations made resulted in the fact that the rock parameter, probably responsible for the loss in ultimate load of the shotcrete lining, were in fact three parameter, occuring at the same time and finally leading to the failure of the shotcrete lining.

The first parameter was the horizontal bedding of the alternating sequences of claystone and sandstone, the second one was the high percentage of claystone (50%) as compared with that of sandstone. The extremely different relationship of the moduli of elasticity of claystone and sandstone, which according to the computation results turned out to be 130/1900 = 0,0684, was the third one of the three parameter mentioned.

In the light of this computation result, the objective of obtaining a numerical judgment of the loss stability can be regarded as achieved.

A numerical analysis was carried out by means of a realistic computation model, applying the method of Decoupled Finite Elements (DFE). By means of this example, the authors want to show that incase of damages in tunnelling as well, modern numerical computation models only supply realistic results, permitting the judgment of probable reasons of damages.

REFERENCES

1 Swoboda, G.: Finite Element Ansätze zur Berechnung gerissener Verbundwerkstoffe. Thesis, Innsbruck University, 1974.

2 Swoboda, G., Laabmayr, F.: Nichtlineare Finite Element Analyse der Auskleidung von Tunneln bei geringer Überdeckung. Bauingenieur, 1979 (54), p. 223-229.

3 Beer, G.: Finite Element, Boundary Element Coupled Analysis of Unbounded Problems in Elastics. Int.J.for Num.Meth. Eng. 19, (1983), p. 567-580.

4 Melan, E.: Spannungszustand der durch eine Einzelkraft im Inneren beanspruchten Halbscheibe. Zeitschrift f. angew. Math. und Mech. (1932), p. 343-346.

5 Swoboda, G.: Finite element analysis of the New Austrian Tunnelling Method (NATM). Conf. on Numerical Methods in Geomechanics, Aachen 1979, p. 582-586.

6 Katone, M.G.: A simple contact-friction interface element with application to buried culverts. Intern. Journal for Numerical and Analytical Methods in Geomechanics 7 (1983), p. 371-384.

7 Goodman, R.E.: Introductory Lecture on Finite Element Analysis for Jointed Rocks. Rock Mechanics, Udine, 1964.

8 Poisel, R.: Diskontinuumsmechanik - Versuch einer Standortbestimmung. Felsbau 1 (1983), p. 9-14.

9 Swoboda, G.: Programmsystem FINAL, Version 6.0.

10 Swoboda, G.: Discontinuum analysis of a tunnel with DECOUPLED FINITE ELEMENT ANALYSIS. Proceedings of ECONMIG 86, Stuttgart, 1986.

Numerical Methods in Geomechanics (Innsbruck 1988), Swoboda (ed.)
© 1989 Balkema, Rotterdam. ISBN 90 6191 809 X

Erratum

Line 14 of the first column on page 1891 should read:

is obtained as $\mu = (0.535^{-1} - 1) \approx 0.87$.

Numerical Methods in Geomechanics (Innsbruck 1988), Swoboda (ed.)
© 1989 Balkema, Rotterdam. ISBN 90 6191 809 X

List of participants

Toshihisa ADACHI
Transportation Eng.
Kyoto University
Yoshida Honmachi Sakyoku
KYOTOUK Japan

Genevieve ADJEDJ
Ecole Centrale de Paris
Grande Voie des Vignes
CHATENAY-MALABRY France

Wolfgang ALDRIAN
Institut für konstruktiven
Tiefbau
Franz-Josef-Str. 18
LEOBEN Austria

rer.nat. H.J. ALHEID
Bundesanstalt für Geowissenschaften
und Rohstoffe
Stilleweg 2
HANNOVER FR Germany

E. E. ALONSO
Universitat Politecnica
de Barcelona
Jordi Girona Salgado, 31
BARCELONA Spain

W. AMBACH
Institut für Med.Physik
Universität Innsbruck
Müllerstr.44
INNSBRUCK Austria

U. ARSLAN
Inst. für Bodenmechanik
TH Darmstadt
Petersenstr. 13
DARMSTADT FR Germany

Akira ASOAKA
Dept. of Geotechnical Eng.
Nagoya University
Chikusa
NAGOYA Japan

D. AUBRY
Ecole Centrale Des Arts et
Manufactures
Grande V.des Vignes
CHATENAY-MALABRY France

Kenneth AXELSSON
Department of Geomechanics
Technical University of Lulea
LULEA Sweden

O. AYDAN
Dept. of Geotechnical Engineering
Nagoya University
Furo-cho, Chikusa-ku
NAGOYA Japan

Genevieve AZEUEDO
Rua Marques de Sao Vicente 225
RIO DE JOUEIRO Brazil

G.M. BABAJANTS
SC ISRM
Volokolamskoe shosse
MOSCOW USSR

H.-P. BADER
Swiss Federal Institute for
Snow and Avalanche Research
WEISSFLUHJOCH Switzerland

Nick BAKER
Elsevier Applied Science
Publishers Ltd.
Linton Road
BARKING UK

Klaas Jan BAKKER
Watersnipstraat 34
DELFT Netherlands

Ezio BALDOVIN
Geotecna Progetti
Via Roncaglia 14
MILANO Italy

B. BAMFORD
President of ISRM
University of Melbourn
PARKVILLE, VIC 3052 Australia

P.K. BANERJEE
Department of Civil Eng.
State Univ. of New York
Buffalo
NEW YORK USA

Ing. Carlo BARDANI
Dept.Ing. Strutturale e
Geotecnica
Viale Monte d'Oro 28
ROMA Italy

G. BARLA
Ce.A.S.
Via Giustiniano 10
MILANO Italy

Manuel Joaquim G. BARROSO
Laboratorio Nacional de Engen-
haria Civil
LISBOA CODEX Portugal

Franciso BATLLE
Tech. University of Catalonya,
Barcelona
Jordi Girona Salgado 31
BARCELONA Spain

G. BAUER
Dept. of Civil Eng.
Carleton University
OTTAWA, ONTARIO Canada

Erich BAUER
Büro Dipl.-Ing.Dr.tech.
Jakob a. thurn 125
PUCH Austria

G. BEER
CSIRO, Division Geomechanics
Privat Bag 3, PO
Indooroopoly
QUEENSLAND Australia

Wolfgang BERWANGER
bpi-Büro für Planung und
Ingenieurtechnik GmbH
Solvayplatz 55
GRENZACH-WYHLEN FR Germany

Bruno BIANCO
Rodio S.p.A.
Casella Postale 7
MELEGNANO Italy

Pierre R. BOLLI
Universite de Liege
Parking 36
LIEGE Belgium

J.R. BOOKER
School of Civil and Mining Eng
The University of Sydney
SYDNEY N.S.W. Australia

Thomas J. BOONE
Cornell University,Ithaca
Hollister Hall
ITHACA USA

Brunetto Mauro BORRI
Politechnico di Torino
Dept.of Structuaral Eng.
Corso Duca degli Abruzzi,34
TORINO Italy

Bard BOSTROM
The Norwegian Inst.of Tech.
Geotechnical Division
Trondheim,Hogskoleringen 7
TRONDHEIM Norway

Eric BOURDAROT
Electrite de France
Rue Ronde 3+5, BP 1034
CHAMBERY France

Castelo J. BRANCO
Laboratorio Nacional de
Engenharia Civil
do Brasil, 101
LISBON Portugal

Markus BRANDTNER
Ingenieurgemeinschaft f.
Geotechnik u. Tunnel bau
Mauracherstrasse 9
SALZBURG Austria

Frank BREINLINGER
Inst. f.Geotechnik, Stuttgart
Pfaffenwaldring 35
STUTTGART FR Germany

C. BREMER
Univ.Dortmund Abt. Bauwesen
Anwend.Numerischer Methoden
August-Schmidt-Str.
DORTMUND 50 FR Germany

Camberto BRISEGHELLA
Istituto Scienza delle
Construzioni
Via Marzolo 9, Univ.di Padova
PADOVA Italy

D. BRUYSSEN
Min.van Verkeer & Waterstraat-
R.W.S.
Kon. Julianaplein 372
AG DEN HAAG Netherlands

John BULL
Department of Civil Engin.
Univ. of Newcastle upun Tyne
TYNE UK

Harvey BURD
Dept.of Eng. Science,
Oxford University
Park Road
OXFORD UK

Giovanni CANETTA
Ce.A.S.
Viale Giustiniano 10
MILANO Italy

J. CARTER
School of Civil and Mining Eng
The University of Sydney
SYDNEY N.S.W. Australia

Floriano CASOLA
Snamprogetti, S. Donato
Viale de Gasperi 16
DONATO Italy

D. CHAN
Dept. of Civil Engineer.
Univ. of Alberta
EDMONTON, AB Canada

Robert CHARLIER
Universite de Liege Service de
Mecanique des Materiaux
6 Quai Banning
LIEGE Belgium

Huei-Tsyr CHEN
National Central University
Department of Civil Engineerin
Chungli
TAIWAN 32054 P.R. China

Royol CHITRADON
Insttitut für Informatik
Universität Innsbruck
Technikerstr. 15
INNSBRUCK Austria

Paul CHOATE
Shell Research b.v. Shell
Exploratie en Productie Lab.
Koninklyke, Postbus 60
RIJSWIJK Netherlands

J.T. CHRISTIAN
Stone & Webster Engineer. Corp
P.O.Box 2325
BOSTON USA

A. CIVIDINI
Dept.of Structural Engineering
Technical Univ.(Politecnico)
Piazza L.da Vinci 32
MILANO Italy

Didier CLOUTEAU
Ecole Central LMSS,Chatenay-Malabry
Grande Voie des Vignes
CHATENAY-MALABRY France

Roberto CONTRO
Dipartimento di Ingegneria
Facolta di Ingegneria d.Trento
Mesiano di Povo
TRENTO Italy

R. COWLING
Mining Research Department
Mount Isa Mines Ltd.
QUEENSLAND Australia

Masantonio CRAVERO
c/o Centro di Studio per i Problemi Minerari
C.so Duca degli Abruzzi 24
TORINO Italy

Domenico CRICCHI
Via D. Costa, 180
VINDOLI Italy

Peter CUNDALL
Consulting Engineer
P.O.Box 195
MARINE ON ST.CROIX USA

H. CZERNY
Bundesministerium für Land- und Forstwirtschaft
Stubenring 12
Wien Austria

Paule D'AZEMAR
Ecole Central LMSS,
Grande Voie des Vignes
CHATENAY-MALABRY France

F.B. DAMJANIC
Edvard Kardelj University
Inst. of Struct and Earth.
Jamova 2 PO Box 579
LJUBLJANA Yugoslavia

Eric DAVALLE
Rue du Centre 80 A
SAINT-SUPLICE Switzerland

D. DE BRUYN
Cent.d'Etude de l'energie nucleaire Studiocentrum voor Kernenergie
BOERETANG 200-MOL Belgium

Fernandes Manuel DE MATOS
Faculdade de Engenharia/Univ. do Porto
Rua dos Bragas
PORTO Portugal

P. DE SIMONE
University of Napoli
Inst.di Tec.delle Fondazioni
Via Claudio 21
NAPOLI Italy

M. DEFFAYET
Centre d'etude des Tunnels
109, Avenue Salvator Allende
BRON France

Raimundo DELGADO
Faculdade de Engenharia da Univ. do Porto
R. dos Bragas
OPORTO Portugal

C.S. DESAI
Dept.of Civil Eng. & Eng.Mech.
University of Arizona
TUCSON USA

E. DETOURNAY
P.O.Box 2710
TULSA USA

Arrigo DI CARLO
AQUATER S.p.A.
Loc. Miralbello
LORENZO IN CAMPO Italy

Janusz M. DLUZEWSKI
Warsaw University of Technolog
Dep. of Civil Engineering
Al. Armii Luddowej 16
WARSAW Poland

Ing. M. DOLEZALOVA
Hydroprojekt
Taborska 31
PRAHA 4 Czechoslovakia

Tilo DÖRING
Lehrstuhl für Fels- und
Gebirgsmechanik
Gustav-Zeuner-Str. 1
FREIBERG DDR

Felix DRAVE
Institute de Mecanique de
Grenoble
Cedex ,B.P.68
ST.MARTIN D'HERES France

H. DUDDECK
Institut für Statik
TU Braunschweig
Pockelstr. 4
BRAUNSCHWEIG FR Germany

M. DYSLI
Ecole Polytechnique Federale
de Lausanne
LAUSANNE Switzerland

Herbert EBNER
University of Innsbruck
Huebe 33
OBERPERFUSS Austria

Claus ERICHSEN
Institut für Grundbau, Boden-
und Felsmechanik
Mies-van-der-Rohe-Str.1
AACHEN FR Germany

A.B. FADEEV
Leningrad Institut of Civil
Eng.
LENINGRAD USSR

Yuan Xun FAN
Inst. of Design of Water Res.
Ministry of Energy
Liupukang
BEIJING P.R. China

Rui FARIA
University of Oporto
OPORTO Portugal

Ali S.M. FAROUQ
Dept. of Mineral Eng.
University of Alberta
EDMONTON Canada

W.D.L. FINN
Dept. of Civil Engineering
University of British Columbia
2324 Main Mall
VANCOUVER, B.C. Canada

Nerio FINOTTI
Snamprogetti,S. Donato
Viale de Gasperi 16
DONATO Italy

F.D. FISCHER
Institut für Mechanik
Montanuniversität Leoben
Franz-Josef-Straße 18
LEOBEN Austria

A.B. FOURIE
University of Queensland
ST.LUCIA Australia

A. FREDRIKSSON
ADG Grundteknik AB
Kapellgrand 3/Boc 4207
STOCKHOLM Sweden

Reinhold FRIEDRICH
Universität Innsbruck,Inst.f.
Wasseru.Tunnelbau
Technikerstrasse 13
INNSBRUCK Austria

M. FUCHSBERGER
TU Graz
Institut für Bodenmechanik
Rechbauerstr. 12
GRAZ Austria

Taher GANABA
Büro Dipl.Ing.Dr.techn.Gerhard
Sauer St.Jakob am Thurn 125
Hallein
PUCH B. Austria

Dietmar GÄRTNER
Bergbau-Forschung GmbH
Abt. Schachtbau
Franz-Fischer-Weg 81
ESSEN 13 FR Germany

L. GAUL
Univ.der Bundeswehr Hamburg
Inst.für Mechanik
Holstenhofweg 85
HAMBURG 70 FR Germany

H. GEISLER
Beton- und Monierbau
Ges.m.b.H.
Bernhard-Höfel-Strasse 11
INNSBRUCK Austria

Antonio GENS
University of Catalunya
E.T.S. Ingenieros de Caminos
Jordi Girona Salgado 31
BARCELONA Spain

G.P. GIANI
Politecnico di Torino
Corso D.D.Abruzzi 24
TORINO Italy

G. GIODA
Dept.of Structural Engineering
Politecnico Di Milano
Piazza L. Da Vinci, 32
MILANO Italy

S. GOBBI
Studio Geotecnico
Via Cintia - Pco S.Paolo is.20
NAPOLI Italy

Dragan GOJGIC
Studio Getecnico S.G.S.,Napoli
Via Cintia-P.co S.Paolo IS. 20
NAPOLI Italy

Johann GOLSER
GEOCONSULT
Sterneckstrasse 55
SALZBURG Austria

Kiasnan GONG
Zhejing University/Karlsruhe Univ.
Rintheimer Hauptstrasse 107
KARLSRUHE FR Germany

Piergiorgio GRASSO
Via Bobbio 12
TORINO Italy

D.V. GRIFFITHS
University of Manchaster
Department of Engineering
Oxford Road
MANCHESTER UK

G. GUDEHUS
Institut für Bodenmechanik
TH Karlsruhe
Kaiserstr. 12
KARLSRUHE FR Germany

P. GUSSMANN
Universität Stuttgart
I G B
Pfaffenwaldring 35
STUTTGART 80 FR Germany

Jörg GUTWALD
Techn.Hochschule Darmstadt
Petersenstrasse 13
DARMSTADT FR Germany

W. HAAS
RIB GmbH
Schulze-Delitzsch-Str. 28
STUTTGART 80 FR Germany

Helmut HAMMER
Inst.f.Bodenmechanik,
Innsbruck University
Silbergasse 18
OBERPERFUSS Austria

M. HAMZA
Consulting Engineers
13, Mohamad Sakeb Street
CAIRO Egypt

Koichi HASHIGUCHI
Kyushu University
Faculty of Agriculture
6-10-1 Hakozaki,Higashi-ku
FUKUOKA Japan

E. HAUGENEDER
Technodat GmbH
Rudolfsplatz 3
WIEN Austria

Manfred HAUPT
Lehrstuhl f. Felsmechanik
Univ.Karlsruhe
Kaiserstr. 12
KARLSRUHE FR Germany

Michael HEILBAUM
Bundesanstalt f. Wasserbau,
Karlsruhe
Kussmaulstrasse 17
KARLSRUHE FR Germany

J.F. HEITZ
Institut de Mecanique
B.P. 68
ST.MARTIN D'HERES France

Rudolf HEUER
Institut f. allg.Mechanik.
TU Wien
Hauptstrasse 8-10
WIEN Austria

Stefan HEUSERMANN
Bundesanstalt f. Geowissen-
schaften u. Rohstoffe
Stilleweg 2
HANNOVER 51 FR Germany

Michael HICKS
University of Manchester
Simon engineering laboratories
Oxford Road
MANCHESTER UK

Yoshio HIRAI
Mokuzai-Dori,Mihara-Cho
Minamikawatsi-Gun
OSAKA Japan

Masayasu HISATAKE
Dept. of Civil Engineering
Kinki University
Higashi-Osaka
KOWAKAE Japan

Günter HOFSTETTER
Techn. Univ. Wien
Inst.f. Festigkeitslehre
Karlsplatz 13
WIEN Austria

J.M. HOHBERG
Inst. f. Baustatik
ETH Hönggerberg
ZÜRICH Switzerland

Klaus HÖNISCH
Lahmeyer International GmbH
Lydnerstr. 22
FRANKFURT FR Germany

Masakuni HORITA
Dept. of Civil Engineering
Kyoto University
KYOTO Japan

G.T. HOULSBY
Dept. of Engineering Science
Oxford University
Parks Road
OXFORD UK

Todor HRISTOV
Institut of Water Problems
Ban Bl. 1 Ul.
Ac. Georgi Bontchev
SOFIA Bulgaria

Qing-Huai HU
P.R. China Society of Nonferrous
Metals
Changsha Institute of Mining
CHANGSHA-HUNAN P.R. China

Wilfried HÜLS
Institut für Bergbausicherheit
Friederikenstr.60
LEIPZIG DDR

P. HUMBERT
58 Boulevard Lefebvre
Paris Cedex 15
PARIS France

Dana HUMPHREY
Dept. of Civil Engineering
Univ. of Maine
103 Boardman Hall
ORONO USA

Bernhard HUPFAUF
Inst. f. bodenmechanik Univ.
Innsbruck
Clemens-Holzmeister-strasse 6
INNSBRUCK Austria

Y. ICHIKAWA
Dept.of Geotechnical Engineer.
Nagoya University
Furo-cho, Chikusa-ku
NAGOYA Japan

A, IIZUKA
Dept. of Civil Engineering
Kyoto University
Yoshida-Hommachi, Sakyo-ku
KYOTO Japan

Toshikazu IMAI
Century Research Centre Corp.
68 4-Chome Kita-kyutaro-machi
OSAKA HIGASHI-KU Japan

Yoshinori INADA
Dept. of Civil Engineering
Ehime University
3 Bunkyocho
MATSUYAMA Japan

A,R. INGRAFFEA
Cornell University
Hollister Hall
Ithaca
NEW YORK 14853 USA

Hans IRSCHIK
Technische Universität Wien
Institut für Allgem. Mechanik
Karlsplatz 13
WIEN Austria

M. IRSHAD
Chief Structural Engineer
DeLeuw, Cather & Comp.
600 Fifth Street
WASHINGTON, D. C. USA

N. JACOB
BGR-Hannover
Stilleweg 2
HANNOVER 51 FR Germany

Zvonimir JAMSEK
Prazkova 8
LJUBLJANA Yugoslavia

Jadatsugu JANAKA
1-1-1 Higasmimita,Tama-Ku,
KAWASAKI Japan

Ing. Pietro JARRE
Politecnico di Torino
Dipart. Ing. Strutturale
Via Mentana 26
TORINO Italy

Max JOHN
ILF-Ingenieursgemeinschaft
Framsweg 16
INNSBRUCK Austria

Manfred KANY
Vestnerstrasse 5B
ZIRNDORF FR Germany

Toshikazu KAWAMOTO
Nogoya University
Chikusa-ku
NAGOYA Japan

Osamu KAWAMOTO
National Research Inst. of
Agricultural Engineering
2-1-2, Kannondai, Tsukuba-si
IBARAKI Japan

N.N. KAZAKOV
Soviet Committee,for International Society for Rock Mech.
Volokolamskoe shosse,2
MOSCOW A-80 USSR

Wilfried KEDDI
Inst. f. Grundbau
RWTH Aachen
Mies-van-der-Rohe-Str. 1
AACHEN FR Germany

Gustav KICHLER
Mayreder,Kraus & Co
Rettenlackstrasse 7
SALZBURG Austria

Stefan KIELBASSA
Institut f. Statik
Techn.Univ. Braunschweig
Beethovenstraße 51
BRAUNSCHWEIG FR Germany

Makoto KIMURA
KYOTO UNIVERSITY
School of Civil Engineering
KYOTO Japan

H. KLAPPERICH
Ing.-Büro
Pacelliallee 5
BERLIN 33 FR Germany

Horst KNATZ
Berbau-Forschung GmbH,Essen
Franz-Fischer-Weg 61
ESSEN FR Germany

A. KNITTEL
Techn.Gerhard Sauer
Jackob am Thurn 125
PUCH Austria

Nigel KNOWLES
WS Atkins Engineering Sciences
Woodcote Grove,Ashley Road
SURREY UK

Akira KOBAYASHI
Hazama-gumi
5-8,Kita-Aoyama 2-Chome,
MINATO-KU - TOKYO Japan

Yukihiro KOHATA
Division of Civil Engineering
Hokkaido University
North 13 West 8
SAPPORO Japan

Yuji KOHGO
National Research Inst. of
Agricultural Engineering
2-1-2, Kannondai,Yatabe-machi
TSUKUBA-GUN Japan

D. KOLYMBAS
Inst.für Bodenmechanik und
Felsmechanik, Univ.Karlsruhe
Postfach Nr. 6380
KARLSRUHE 1 FR Germany

Frank T. KÖNIG
Philipp Holzmann AG,Hannover
Postfach 29 27
HANNOVER FR Germany

Rat . Franz KÖNIG
Bundesministerium für
Land- und Forstwirtschaft
Stubenring 1
WIEN Austria

D. KÖNKE
Bundeswehrhochschule
Werner Heisenberg Weg 39
NEUBIBERG FR Germany

A.P. KOOIJMAN
TU Delft
Dept. of Civil Engineering
P.O. Box 5048
DELFT Netherlands

M.Sc. Mauri KOSKINEN
Tampere University of
Technology
P.O. Box 527
TAMPERE Finland

Nikolaos KOUTSABELOULIS
BP Research Centre
Chertsey Road
SUNBURY-ON-THAMES UK

D. KOVACIC
Geoexpert
B. Domany 6
ZAGREB Yugoslavia

P. KULATILAKE
Dept. of Mining & Geol. Eng.
Univ. of Arizona
TUCSON USA

H. KULHAWY
School of Civil Engineering
Cornell University
Hollister Hall
ITHACA, NEW YORK USA

Franz LAABMAYR
Zivilingenieur
Preishartlweg 4
SALZBURG Austria

P.V. LADE
Rm.3173,Engineering I,School
of Eng.& Appl.Science
University of California
LOS ANGELES USA

Pauleen LANE
University of Mancvhester
Oxford Road
OXFORD UK

M.A. LANGE
Alfred-Wegener-Inst.
Columbusstraße
BREMERHAVEN FR Germany

Ragnar LARSSON
Chamlmers Univ.of Technology
Dept. of Structural Mechanics
GÖTEBORG Sweden

Nigel LAST
British Petroleum Company
KSEPL
Chertsey Road
MIDDLESEX UK

David LAUENDER
19,Anslow GDNS,Jver Heath
JVER,BUCKS SLOOBW UK

Alberto LEDESMA
University of Catalunya
E.T.S. Ingenieros de Caminos
Jordi Girona Salgado 31
BARCELONA Spain

Ingegnere, A. LEMBO-FAZIO
University of Rome,Inst.Arte
Mineraria
Via Eudosiana 18
ROMA Italy

Erich LETHMAYER
UNIDO Programme for Construct.
Systems for Developing Countr.
P.O. Box 400
WIEN Austria

A.Y.T. LEUNG
University of Hongkong
Dept.of Civil and Struct.Eng.
HONGKONG
Hongkong

C.O. LI
University of Manchester
Dept. of Civil Engineering
Oxford Road
MANCHESTER UK

Jakob LIKAR
Institute of Mathematics,
Physik and Mechanics
Tesarska 10
LJUBLJANA Yugoslavia

Yun-mei LIN
Northeast Univ.of Technology
Chinese Society of Rock Mech.
Dept.of Mining Engineering
SHENYANG/LIAONING P.R. China

Eckart LINDNER
BPI Büro für Planung
und Ingenieurtechnik GmbH
Solvayplatz 55
GRENZACH-WYHLEN FR Germany

Michael LINSER
Claudiastr. 20
INNSBRUCK Austria

Zhuhua LIU
Inst. of Geology
Academia Sinica
P.O.Box 634
BEIJING P.R. China

Huaiheng LIU
Xian Mining Institute
14 Yanta Road
XIAN SHAANXI P.R. China

Jun LIU
Academia Sinica
Institut of Geology
P.O. Box 634
BEIJING P.R. China

Zhong LIU
Mining Dept. of Chongqing Univ
Chongqing University
CHONGQING-SICHUAN P.R. China

Antonio LLORET
University of Catalunya
E.T.S. Ingenieros de CamiBnos
4 Jordi Girona Salgado 31
BARCELONA Spain

K.W. LO
Civil Engineering Dept.,
National Univ. of Singapore
Kent Ridge Campus
SINGAPORE
Singapore

Peiyan LU
Shougauling,Shahe
GUANGZHOU P.R.China

Jaroslav MACKERLE
Linköping Inst. of Technology
Dept. of Mechanical Eng.
LINKÖPING Sweden

Manfred MACKERT
Stiftsbogen 75
MÜNCHEN FR Germany

Ingo MADER
Universität Innsbruck
Technikerstr. 13
INNSBRUCK Austria

Claudio Fernando MAHLER
Federal University of Rio
Coppe-UFRJ
RIO DE JANEIRO Brazil

Joh. MAJER
Institut für Festigkeitslehre
und Flächentragwerke
Technikerstrasse 13
INNSBRUCK Austria

M. MAKSIMOVIC
Faculty of Civil Engineering
B. Revolucije 73
BEOGRAD Yugoslavia

Mimura MAMORU
Disas.Prev.Res.Inst.
Kyoto University,
Gokasho Uji
KYOTO Japan

Kanatani MAMORU
Central Research Inst. of
Electric power Industry
Chiba-Ken
ABIKO Japan

Philippe MARCHINA
Institut de Mechanique
de Grenoble
ST.MARTIN D'HERES France

Giv.Eng. Pavao MAROVIC
Gradevinski Institut
Veselina Maslese bb
SPLIT Yugoslavia

Donald MASON
Taisei Cooperation
Civil Engineering Dept.
P.O.Box 4001,Shinjuku-Ku
TOKYO Japan

Tamotsu MATSUI
Dept.of Civil Engineering
Osaka University
2-1,Yamadaoka, Suita
OSAKA Japan

Peter MATT
Vorarlberger Illwerke
Batlockstrasse
SCHRUNS Austria

Patric McCULLEN
Electricity Suppy Board
IRL.
18-21 St. Stephen's Green
DUBLIN Ireland

Francisco MEDINA
P.O. Box 10211
BERKELEY USA

M. MEHL
Büro Prof.Dr. Sickl
Blindengasse 26
WIEN Austria

Helmut MEISSNER
Univ. Kaiserslautern
Fachg.Grundb.u.Bodenmechanik
Pfaffenbergstr.
KAISERSLAUTERN FR Germany

Rudolf MELBINGER
Bundesministerium f.Land-u.
Forstwirtschaft
Stubenring 12
WIEN Austria

Joshua MERRIT
P.O.Box 1206
REDLAND USA

Wolfgang MERTZ
Universität Innsbruck
Technikerstr. 13
INNSBRUCK Austria

Klaus METTIER
Elektrowatt, Ingenieuruntern.
Postfach
ZÜRICH Switzerland

Alkis E. MITAKIDIS
BAM-Bundesanstalt für Material
prüfung, Labor 2.32
Unter den Eichen 87
BERLIN 45 FR Germany

Hormoz MODARESSI
B.R.G.M.(bureau de Recherche
Geologiques et Minieres)
Avenue de Concyr,B.P.6009
ORLEANS France

M. MOHKAM
Ecole Nationale des Travaux
Publics de l'Etat
Rue Maurice Audin
VAULX-EN-VELIN France

F. MOLENKAMP
Delft Geotechnics
P.O. BOX 69
DELFT Netherlands

Luigi MONGIOVI
Univ.di Roma "Tor Vergata",
Dipart.di Ing.Civil Edile
Via Orazio Raimondo
ROMA Italy

Jaques M.A. MONNET
Universite de Grenoble
I.R.I.G.M.-U.S.T.M.G.
Postbox 68
ST.MARTIN D'HERES France

James E. MONSEES
Parson Brinckerhoff Quad and
Diuglas .
548 south spring street
LOS ANGELES USA

Ian MOORE
Univ.of Newcastle
Dept.of Civil Eng.
SHORTLAND NSW Australia

Seiji MORIKAWA
KAJIMA CORPORATION
2-7,Motoakasaka,1-chome
MINATOKU - TOKYO Japan

L.W. MORLAND
University of East Anglia
NORWICH UK

Nobuchika MOROTO
Hachinohe Inst.of Techn.
Dept.of Civil Eng.
88-1 Obiraki Myo
HACHINOHE/AOMORI Japan

Janze MRAMOR
Finzgarieva 12
TITOVO Yugoslavia

Z. MROZ
Inst.of Fundamental Technology
Res., Polish Acad. of Science
Swistokvzyska 21
WARSAW Poland

David MUIRWOOD
Dept. of Civil Engineering
University of Glasgow
Ranking Building
GLASGOW UK

Peter Jürgen MÜLLER
Interggeo-Consultant
Robingstrasse 26 a
SALZBURG Austria

Akira MURAKAMI
Dept. of Agrigcult.Engineering
Kyoto University
Kitashirakawa-oiwake-cho
SAKYO-KU, KYOTO Japan

Hidekazu MURATA
Yamaguchi University
Faculty of Engineering
Department of Civil Eng.
UBE TOKIWADAI Japan

Teruo NAKAI
Dept.of Environmental Eng.
Nagoya Institute of Technology
Gokishocho, Showakuu
NAGOYA Japan

D. J. NAYLOR
University College of Swansea
Dept. of Civil Engineering
SWANSEA UK

Ferydun NAZARI
Chair of geotechnica TU Brno
Barvicova 85
BRNO Czechoslovakia

Walther NETZER
University of Innsbruck
Technikerstrasse 13
INNSBRUCK Austria

O. NEUNER
c/o Zivilingenieurbüro
Dr. H Passer
Adamgasse 1a
INNSBRUCK Austria

Akira NISHIHARA
Dept.of Civil Eng.
Fukuyama Univ.
Matsunagacho
FUKUYAMA Japan

B.K. NOREL
Internnational Society for
Rock Mechanics (SC ISRM)
Volokolamskoe shosse,2,
MOSCOW,A-80 USSR

Roberto NOVA
Politecnico di Milano Dept.di
Ingegneria Strutturale
Piazza Leonardo da Vinci 32
MILANO Italy

Giorgio NOVATI
Politehnico di Milano Dipart.
di Ingegneria Strutturale
Piazza Leonardo da Vinci,32
MILANO Italy

Hidetoshi OCHIAI
Dept.of Civil Eng.
Kyushu University
6-10-1 Hakozaki
FUKUOKA Japan

Eiji OGISAKO
SHIMIZU Construction Co.Ltd.
No.16-1, Kyobashi,2-Chome
Chuo-ku
TOKYO Japan

Masayuki OHNAMI
Kozo Keikaku Engineering Inc.
38-13,4-chome hon-cho,Nakanoku
TOKYO Japan

Hideki OHTA
Dept.of Civil Eng.
Kanazawa University
2-40-20 Kodatsuno
KANAZAWA Japan

Fusao OKA
Dept.of Constr.Eng.
Gifu University
1-1, Yanagido
GIFU Japan

Atsuo ONOUE
Institute of Technology,
Shimizu Construction co., LTD.
No.4-17, Etchujima, 3-Chome
TOKYO Japan

Michael OSTERMANN
Universität Innsbruck
Technikerstrasse 13
INNSBRUCK Austria

B. OSTERMEIER
TU München
Arcisstr. 21
MÜNCHEN 2 FR Germany

Odik OZANAM
Coyne et Bellier
Bureau d'Ingenieurs Conseils
5 Rue d'Heliopolis
PARIS France

G.N. PANDE
Dept. of Civil Engineering
Univ.College of Swansea
Singleton Park
SWANSEA UK

Ing. Paolo PAOLIANI
ENEA-DISP
Via Vitaliano Brancati 48
ROM Italy

W.G. PARISEAU
Dept.of Mining Engineering
Univ. of Utah,
SALT LAKE CITY USA

Manuel PASTOR
Centro de Estudios y Experim.
de Obras Publicas
Alfonso XII, 3
MADRID Spain

Lars PERSSON
ADC Grundteknik AB
Box 17026
STOCKHOLM Sweden

Eric PICCUEZZU
Ecole Central de Paris
Grande Voie des Vignes
CHATENAY-MALABRY France

Lutz PISARSKY
TU-Braunschweig
Marienstr.45
BRAUNSCHWEIG FR Germany

R. PÖTTLER
ILF Consulting Engineers
Framsweg 16
INNSBRUCK Austria

Marc PRABUCKI
Ruhr Universität Bochum
Universitätsstraße 150
BOCHUM FR Germany

Daniel PRADEL
University of California
Civil Eng. Department
405 Hilgard Avenua
LOS ANGELES USA

Tej B.S. PRADHAN
Geo Research Institut
Osaka Soil Test Laoratory
3-1-23 Nishi Honmachi u
OSAKA Japan

Reinhard PROMPER
Tauernkraftwerke AG,
Reinerstrasse 29
SALZBURG Austria

Olgierd PULA
Geotechnical Institute
Wroclaw Tehcnical University
Pl. Grunwaldzki 9
WROCLAW Poland

Jari PUTTONEN
Imatran Voima Oy
Department of Civil Eng.
P.O. Box 138
HELSINKI Finland

Ian PYRAH
University of Sheffield
Dept.of Civil and Struct.Eng.
Mappin Street
SHEFFIELD UK

Yuanye QIAN
Jiang-Xi Institute of
Metallurgy
GAN-ZHOU P.R. China

Ugo RABAGLIATI
Geoanalysis s.r.l.,
Corso Galieo Ferraris,71
TORINO Italy

Walter RAHN
Ing.-Geol.Institut
Dipl.Ing. S.Niedermeyer
WESTHEIM FR Germany

M.F. RANDOLPH
The University of Western Australia
NEDLANDS Australia

M.B. REED
Mathematics Dept.,
Brunel University
UXBRIDGE UK

N. RENGERS
ITC
P.O.Box 6
ENSCHEDE Netherlands

Renato RIBACCHI
Univ. of Roma, Dipart. Igegneria Strutturale e Geotechnica
Via Montedoro 28
ROME Italy

Frank ROGMAN
Kaiserslautern/Inst. f. Bodenmechanik und Grundbau
Erwin Schrödingerstr. 14
KAISERSLAUTERN FR Germany

G. ROMBACH
Univ.Karlsruhe, Abt.Massivbau
Postfach 6980
KARLSRUHE FR Germany

Tatiana ROTONDA
Univ. of Rome,Dipart. di Ingegneria Strutturale e Geotecnic
Via Montedoro 28
ROME Italy

R.K. ROWE
University of Western Ontario
Geotechnical Research Centre
Faculty of Engineering Science
LONDON ONTARIO Canada

K. RUNESSON
c/o Stein Sture University of Colorado
Campus Box 428
BOULDER USA

Kurt-J. RUSERT
Stadt Dortmund
Stadtbahnbauamt
Victoriastr. 15
DORTMUND 1 FR Germany

Detlef RÜTZ
Hochschule f. Architektur u. Bauwesen
Geschwister-scholl-Strasse
WEIMAR DDR

J. RYDER
Rock Mech.Laborat.,Chamber of Mines of S.A.Research Organis.
P.O.Box 91230
AUCKLAND PARK South Africa

Anders RYNER
ADG Grundteknik AB
Box 17026
STOCKHOLM Sweden

C. SAGASETA
University of Santander
Avd. de Los Castros, s/n
SANTANDER Spain

A. SAKAI
Saga University
Dept. of Civil Engineering
1 Honjo Saga
HONJO SAGA Japan

Segundo Fernando SAN
Hidroelectrica Espanola,S.A.
Paseo de Castellana, 1
MADRID Spain

Shad SARGAND
Ohio University
Dept.of Civil Engineering
Stocker Center
2979 OHIO USA

Tadanobu SATO
Disaster Prevention Res. Inst.
Kyoto University
Gokasho, Uji
KYOTO Japan

Ohtsuka SATORU
Dept. of Geotechnical Eng.
Nagoya University
J 464 Chikusa
NAGOYA Japan

Hermann SCHAD
Univ. Stuttgart
Institut für Grundbau
Postfach 80 11 40
STUTTGART FR Germany

K. SCHIKORA
Lehrst. f. Baustatik
TU München
Arcisstr. 21
MÜNCHEN 2 FR Germany

Klaus SCHMID
Ing.-Gemeinschaft Feizlmayr
Framsweg 16
INNSBRUCK Austria

Günther SCHMID
Bauingenieurwesen,Ruhr-Univ.
BOCHUM FR Germany

Uwe SCHMIDT
Kavernen Bau-und Betriebs-Gmbh
Roscherstrasse 7
HANNOVER FR Germany

Harald SCHMIDT
Dipl.-Ing.P.Fritsch,Dipl.-Ing.
Gerd Chiari,Ziviling.f.Bauwese
Diesterweggasse 1/6
WIEN Austria

Johann SCHMIEDER
bpi-Büro f. Planung u.
Ingenieurtechnik GmbH
Solvayplatz 55
GRENZACH-WYHLEN FR Germany

W. SCHOBER
Universität Innsbruck
Institut für Bodenmechanik,
Felsmechanik und Grundbau
Technikerstr. 13
INNSBRUCK Austria

G.I. SCHUELLER
Universität Innsbruck,
Institut für Mechanik
Technikerstr. 13
INNSBRUCK Austria

H.F. SCHWEIGER
Technische Univeristät Graz
Inst. für Bodenmechanik
Rechbauerstr.12
GRAZ Austria

A.P.S. SELVADURAI
Dept. of Civil Eng.
Carleton Univ.
C.J. Mackenzie Eng. Bldg.
OTTAWA, ONTARIO Canada

Yasuhiro SHIMIZU
Meijo University,Dept.of Civil
Eng.Nagoya
Shiogamachi,1-chome,Tenpaku-ku
NAGOYA,AICHI Japan

T. SHINOKAWA
Engineering Research Institut
Sato Kogyo Co., Ltd.
47-3,Sanda,Atsugi,
KANANGAWA Japan

Tadakiko SHIOMI
Takenaka Komuten Co.
2-5-14, Minami-Suna Koto-Ku
TOKYO Japan

Oskar SIGL
Institut f.Konstruktiven Tief-
bau,Montanuniversität Leoben
Parkstrasse 27
LEOBEN Austria

SIMONETTI
Aquater S.p.A.,San Lorenzo
Via Miralbello,53
SAN LORENZO IN C. Italy

Luciano SIMONI
Instituto di Scienza e Tecnica
delle Costruzioni
Via Marzolo 9
PADOVA Italy

H.J. SIRIWARDANE
Dept.of Civil Engineering
West Virginia University
P.O.Box 6101
MORGANTOWN USA

S.W. SLOAN
The University of Newcastle
NEW SOUTH WALES Australia

J. SMALL
School of Civil and Mining Eng
The University of Sydney
SYDNEY N.S.W. Australia

I.M. SMITH
Simon Engineering Laboratory
University of Manchester
Oxford Road
MANCHESTER UK

Renald SOYEAUX
Universität Stuttgart
Institut für Wasserbau
Pfaffenwaldring 61
STUTTGART,80 FR Germany

S.E.J. SPIERENBURG
Delft Geotechnics
P.O. Box 69
DELFT Netherlands

Miljenko SRKOC
Gradevinsky Institut
J. Rakuse 1
ZAGREB Yugoslavia

R. STARK
Institut für Festigkeitslehre
Univ.Innsbruck
Technikerstr. 13
INNSBRUCK Austria

Kurt STAUDTMEISTER
Inst. f. Unterirdisches Bauen,
Univ.Hannover
Welfengarten 1
HANNOVER FR Germany

D. STOLLE
McMaster University
Dept.of Civil Engineering
HAMILTON/ONTARIO Canada

J. SULEM
Ecole Nationale des Ponts et
Chaussees
Central 2 La Courtine Boit.105
NOISY L. G. CEDE France

F.T. SUORINENI
U.S.T. School of Mines
Department of Geology & Survey
P.O. Box 237
TARKWA Ghana

Gunter SWOBODA
University of Innsbruck
Technikerstr. 13
INNSBRUCK Austria

Nobuo TAKAGI
Blackwater
67 Bloomsbury Way
SURREY UK

Nobuo TAKAGI
Blackwater
67 Bloomsbury Way
SURREY UK

Y. TANAKA
Osaka Office Itochu Bldg.
Century Research Centre Corp.
4-68 Kita-Kyutaro-Machi
HIGASHI-KU Japan

C. TANIMOTO
Dept.of Civil Engineering
Kyoto University
Yoshida-Hommachi, Sakyo-ku
KYOTO Japan

Omachi TATSUO
Tokyo Institute of Technology
4259 Nagatsuta,Midoriku,Kanaja
YOKOHAMA Japan

S. TAYLOR
Brighton,Sussex,83,
Carlyle St.
BRIGHTON UK

Hans TEUNISSEN
Delft Soil Mechanics
Laboratory
Postbox 69
AB DELFT Netherlands

Peter B.H. THE
Margarethalaan 515
DEN HAAG Netherlands

M. THIERCELIN
Schlumberger Research Lmtd.
PO Box 153
CAMBRIDGE UK

Tamano TOMIO
J Sennan Gun,Osaka
Ogaito Kumatori-cho
OSAKA Japan

Michal TOPOLNICKI
Institute of Soil and Rock M.
University of Karlsruhe
Postfach 6380
KARLSRUHE FR Germany

Simon TORTIKE
Univ.of Alberta
Dept.of Mining,Metallurgica
EDMONTON Canada

Charles TRAUTMANN
Techn. Universität München
Baumbachstrasse 7
MÜNCHEN FR Germany

S. TSUCHIYAMA
Chubu Electric Power Co.
20-1,Kitasekiyama, Odaka-cho
MIDORI-KU,NAGOYA Japan

Y. UETA
The University of Tokushima
2-1,Minamijosanjima-cho
TOKUSHIMA Japan

Keizo UGAI
Gunma University
Dept. of Civil Eng.
Gunma 376
KIRYU-SHI Japan

Professor S. UKHOV
Moscow Civil Engineering
Institut
Yaroslavskoe shosse 26
MOSCOW USSR

S. VALLIAPPAN
Dept. of Civil Engineering
University of New South Wales
P.O. Box 1
KENSINGTON Australia

Harry van Langen
Technical University Delft
Stevinweg 1
DELFT Netherlands

Adriaan J. van Seters
Fugro-McClelland Engineers B.V
P.O. Box 63
LEIDSCHENDAM Netherlands

L. VANDAMME
Dowell Schlumberger Incorp.
P.O.Box 2710
TULSA USA

I.G. VARDOULAKIS
Dept.of Civil & Mineral Eng.
University of Minnesota
122 Civil & Mineral Eng. Bld.
MINNEAPOLIS USA

Solano VEGA
T.U. München
Roseggerstr. 5
MÜNCHEN FR Germany

P. A. VERMEER
Delft University of Technology
Dept. of Civil Engineering
1 Stevinweg
DELFT Netherlands

M. VINCHES
Ecole des Mines de Paris
Institut des Materiaux
6, Avenue de Clavieres
ALES CEDEX France

N.P. VLOKH
"Hydroproject" Institut
Volokolamskoe shosse 2
MOSCOW USSR

Johannes VOGT
Universität Kaiserslautern
Postfach 3049
KAISERSLAUTERN FR Germany

Günter WAAS
c/o Hochtief AG
Abt.Kerntechn.Ing.Bau
Postfach 3189
FRANKFURT FR Germany

Dip.Ing. Johannes WAGENEDER
Geoconsult Ingenieurbüro
Sterneckstr.55
SALZBURG Austria

Harald WAGNER
Mayreder Consult GmbH
Sophiengutstr. 20
LINZ Austria

Friedrich WALL
Universtät Innsbruck
Technikerstrasse 13
INNSBRUCK Austria

C. WALTHER
DBE
Woltorfer Str. 74
PEINE FR Germany

Richard WAN
University of Alberta,Dept.of
Civil Eng. Elec.Eng.Bldg.
Edmonton
ALBERTA Canada

Kohei WATANABE
Inst.of Technology, Shimizu
Construction Lo, Ltd.
No.4-17, Etchujima 3-chome
TOKYO Japan

Wolfgang WEIGERT
Expert/Court of Law
Petrus Klotzgasse 13-15
WIEN Austria

H. WERNER
MPA-TUM
Arcisstr. 21
MÜNCHEN 2 FR Germany

N.E. WIBERG
Dept.of Struct.Mechanics
Chalmers University of Techn.
GOTEBORG Sweden

M. WICKE
Institut für Stahlbeton- und
Massivbau
INNSBRUCK Austria

Dr Rolf WIEDERHOFER
Tiwag
Grieß 45
LEISACH Austria

Anthony WILLIAMS
Kingston Polytechnic,Surrey
Penrhyn Rd.
KINGSTON UK

Heinz WIMMER
Universität Innsbruck
Technikerstrasse 13
INNSBRUCK Austria

D. WINSELMANN
Ingenieurbüro Duddeck Partner
Inst.f.Statik
Pockelstraße 7
BRAUNSCHWEIG FR Germany

Erich WISSER
Bochstraße 3
BREGENZ Austria

Ing. Henk WITLOX
SHELL Reasarch
Thorton Research Centre
P.O. Box 1
CHESTER UK

W. WITTKE
Institut für Grundbau, Boden-
und Felsmechanik TH AACHEN
Mies-van-der-Rohe-Str. 1
AACHEN FR Germany

John P. WOLF
Elektrowatt Ingenieur-
unternehmen AG
Postfach
ZÜRICH Switzerland

S. YAJIMA
Taisei Corporation
Kathmandu
P.O. Box 3687
JAMAL Japan

A. YASHIMA
Disaster Prevention Res.Inst.
Kyoto University
GOKASYO UJI Japan

Ikuo YASUKAWA
Fushimi Technical High School
15-3 Suzutsuka-cho, Fukakusa
KYOTO FUSHIMI-KU Japan

Yukimitsu YOKOYAMA
Utsunomiya University
2753 Ishii-machi,Tochigi Pref.
UTSUNOMIYA Japan

M. ZAMAN
School of Civil Eng.
University of Oklahoma
202 West Boyd Street, Room 334
NORMAN OKLAHOMA USA

Schiebenhöfer Dirk ZANDER
Inst. f. Unterirdisches Bauen
Univ. Hannover
Welfengarten 1
HANNOVER FR Germany

Gerald ZENZ
Tauernkraftwerke
Rainerstraße 29
SALZBURG Austria

Jingsheng ZHANG
Hydro-Power Construction
MWREP
BEIJING P.R. China

De-cheng ZHANG
Physics departement of Ningxia
Univ.
YINCHUAN - NINGXIA P.R. China

Jiyu ZHOU
Changsha Instittute of Mining
Research
Hunan
CHANGSHA P.R. China

Franc ZIGMAN
Mining Inst. Ljubljana
Prazakova 8
LJUBLJANA Yugoslavia

Th. ZIMMERMANN
Zace Services SA
Ingenieurs-Conseils Associes
Case Postale 2
LAUSANNE 15 Switzerland

Numerical Methods in Geomechanics (Innsbruck 1988), Swoboda (ed.)
© 1989 Balkema, Rotterdam. ISBN 90 6191 809 X

Author index

Advertisement

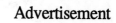

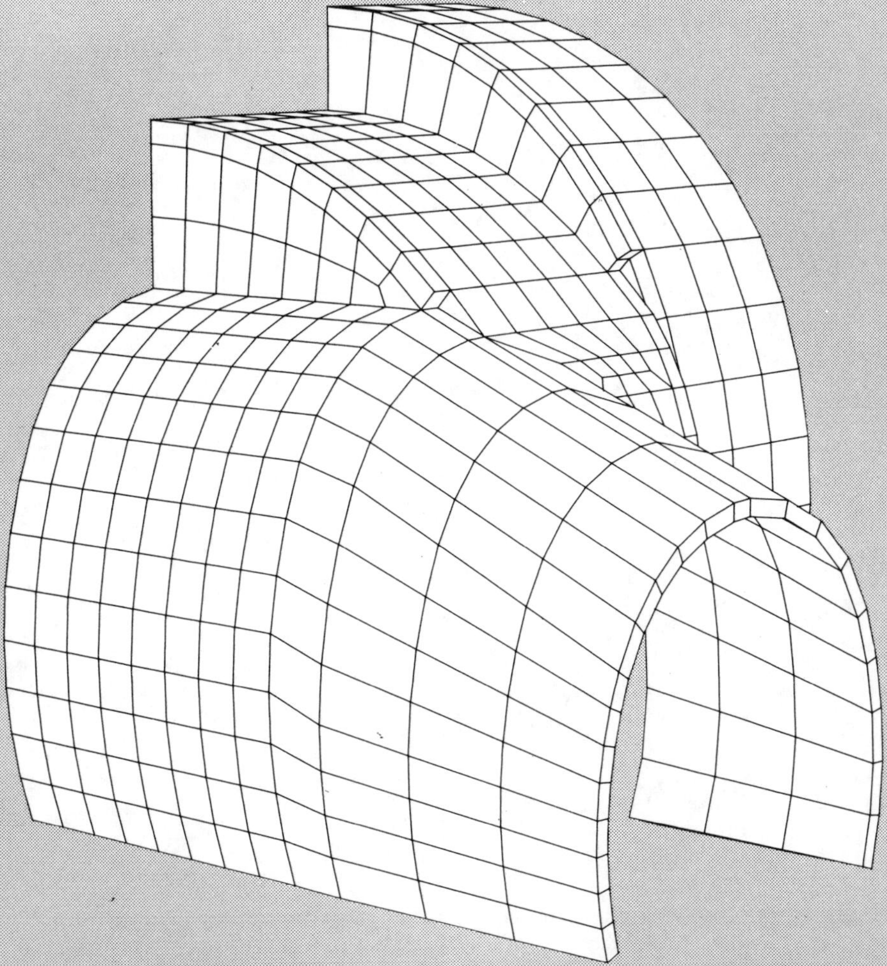